ABOUT

Nick Hall, Ph.D. is a medical scientist and professional speaker, who for over 30 years has conducted groundbreaking studies linking the mind and body. This research has been published in over 150 periodicals and featured by the national and international media, including CBS' *60 Minutes*, the BBC's *Nova* series, and the Emmy Award-winning program *Healing and the Mind*, aired by PBS. He also has been the recipient of two prestigious Research Scientist Development Awards, which the National Institutes of Health grants only to the top scientists in the United States. Nick is no stranger, as well, to the more pragmatic aspects of dealing with change and with making difficult choices. After earning his way through college wrestling alligators and milking rattlesnakes, he worked as an intelligence-operative for the U.S. Government. He also led a *National Geographic*-sponsored expedition to the West Indies, where he studied mass-stranding behavior in whales. While working in the islands, he endured the Marxist revolution in Grenada and the La Soufriere volcano eruption in St. Vincent. His practical insights for coping with change and adversity have been shaped over a span of nearly four decades. For example, in 1968, he became the first person to complete the grueling Baja 1,000-mile off-road race on a bicycle; while in 2006, he completed WaterTribe's Ultimate Florida Challenge in a kayak. This 1200 mile nautical race, which included a 40-mile portage, has been described by *Times of London* as, "the most dangerous small boat race in the world." At his Saddlebrook Resort headquarters in Florida, Dr. Hall presents highly successful workshops and motivational programs for some of America's leading corporations.

Visit **www.drnickhall.com** for information about his programs, books, and audio series.

WINNING THE STRESS CHALLENGE

By Nick Hall, Ph.D.

Published by:
Health Dateline Press
707 West River Drive
Temple Terrace, FL 33617

First printing, September 2006.
Second printing with revisions, February 2009.

Nick Hall, Ph.D.
Winning The Stress Challenge
ISBN 978-0-615-27512-3

Cover art by John C. McMillan

ACKNOWLEDGMENTS

I've drawn from so many sources of information and personal experiences in putting this book together that I am at a loss to know where to begin in thanking all those who have contributed to this effort. The one exception is my loving wife, Hazel, whose contributions clearly outshine all others. Her patience and understanding while I was researching this topic kept me grounded and sane. This included keeping the home fires stoked while I was off on some adventure, testing the ideas discussed in this book. Also my two daughters, Rachele and Stephanie, each of whom has performed alligator wrestling shows with their dad at the Black Hills Reptile Gardens in South Dakota. They've also shared cross-country motorcycle and bicycle adventures with me, which is how I learned that the rules of dealing with stress change when loved ones are involved. I'm also indebted to the wisdom and example set by my mother, Eileen, who, for 93 years, behaved like a woman in her twenties, thereby, serving as an inspiration for all who encountered her. Finally, my stepfather, Max, whose hard work and dedication to his adopted family were unparalleled.

A large number of people have assisted with the preparation of the material used in writing this book. I'm especially indebted to Barbara Furtek, who expertly set about the task of correcting the numerous grammatical blunders and misspellings, which were scattered about draft copies of this effort. I'd also like to acknowledge her astute ability to spot statements with meanings other than the ones intended, along with the literary solutions. In addition, Betty LeDoux-Morris, a Certified Meeting Professional, has been instrumental in forging the corporate connections that have kept this book grounded in pragmatism.

Others have helped shape some of the described concepts. The conclusions of Dr. Irv Dardik, expressed in his Wavenergy Theory, have made me realize that stress is good for you and that it is only when stress is unabated by recovery that health will be impaired. Dr. Phil Hayden's research and insights into the ways elite FBI agents cope with stress under extreme circumstances have taught me that academic models have little relevance when you find yourself in a rapidly failing environment. I am particularly grateful for having had the opportunity to work with Dr. Jim Loehr, whose insights pertaining to stress and performance in athletes have demonstrated that there are viable strategies which can be employed to prevent stress from impacting performance. Some of the strategies involving exercise and acting are based upon those insights. I'm particularly grateful for the recommendations of Dr. Gerald Iwerks, a professional mediator, whose discussions on the subject of conflict have proved invaluable in formulating the strategies for coping with adversity. Dr. Blake Anderson served as a consultant and contributor to the audio program *Prescription for Burnout*, parts of which have been incorporated into this book. Also, Paula Stahil, who edited an earlier edition of this book, titled *Orchestrating the Mind and Body*. Finally, I am indebted to the professional insights of Geneele Crump, a highly skilled Licensed Clinical Social Worker, who has made valuable suggestions pertaining to the recommended behavioral-interventions and has assisted with the editing and organization of the chapters.

In addition to acknowledging those who gave direct input while I was writing this book, I wish to acknowledge those who indirectly provided assistance. Steve Isaac, founder of the organization WaterTribe, has provided me with the opportunity to test under extreme conditions while participating in WaterTribe-sponsored Challenges the recommendations I describe in these pages. Also, I wish to acknowledge my many friends at Nightingale-Conant, publishers of my audio programs, from which some of the material in this book has been drawn. Finally, I wish to acknowledge the National Institutes of Health, which, over a span of nearly four decades, has provided generous funding for my own mind-body research, as well as the research of others, which has been incorporated into the following chapters.

TABLE OF CONTENTS

INTRODUCTION

Former prisoners of war and the survivors of concentration camps who showed adeptness in coping with stress shared certain characteristics in common according to research carried out at Stanford University:

❑ They did not surrender or give up their spirit.

❑ They maintained a sense of control no matter how bad it got. Despite everything going on around them, they could still control their own thoughts.

❑ They attributed some important meaning to their suffering and pain.

❑ They focused on good or positive things throughout each day. For example, "I got some food today," or "I didn't get beaten today."

❑ They maintained a strong sense of purpose and resolve to make it through the ordeal.

This research clearly shows that it is how you respond to the challenges you face that determines their impact upon your health. Your perception, your cognitive appraisal, and your interpretation are what matter most. These are the fundamental skills you need to have in order to win the stress challenge. And where do they come from? Simply put, they are acquired. Taking responsibility for how you react to the things that happen to you is the first step. Choosing not to see yourself as a victim and maintaining control is step two. Step three is to intentionally and habitually start thinking and acting in ways that keep you positive, engaged, empowered, and resilient. This is the winning formula, and this book will show you how to make it work for you.

You will begin by identifying the amount and types of stress that currently exist in your life. Next, you will learn the basic skills you'll need to identify the warning signs so you can take preventative action and reduce the probability that stressors even will arise. Then you will be guided through a series of scientifically grounded strategies to help you better manage life's challenges. Skeptical? Then you can delve into the references at the end of this book, which will provide whatever documentation you are seeking.

No two people respond in the same way to a stressor, and no two people will benefit in the same way from a stress management program. Protocols have to be highly customized to meet your specific needs. This program is designed to provide you with the tools to identify the root causes of your stress-related problems as well as a menu of healthy responses so that you can customize your own personal program.

Many of the sections contain questions to help you distinguish between the stressor, your perception of events, your emotional response, and some of the secondary issues such as inherent conflicts between your response and your value system. Take time to carefully consider each question, and write or verbalize the answer to yourself or a trusted friend. This process will enable you to organize your thoughts. You will also gain insights by viewing the problem from a fresh perspective. Instead of simply responding to the emotional fallout, you will now have an opportunity to view the problem through the spoken or written word. If nothing else, just this process is healing because you are gaining a measure of control. You are no longer helpless. You soon will come to realize that you alone can empower or derail your healing system.

Identifying the key components of your stress response through introspection, however, is not enough unless you take steps to create a healthier response. This book offers a variety of options. You will be provided with guidelines to engage in healthier dietary habits, to improve the quality of your sleep, and to use exercise to train for stress recovery. The health benefits of friendship, steps you can take to cope better with burnout, and ways to energize yourself also will be discussed.

WHAT ARE YOUR STRESSORS?

One of the greatest arenas for stress for many people is their work. Complete this brief questionnaire to determine if you might be suffering from job-related stress.

1) Do you believe that you have very little control over circumstances at work?
2) Could you do a better job with more time in which to do it?
3) Do you have difficulty making decisions at work?
4) Are you performing below your full potential?
5) Has new technology (computers, for example) exceeded your capacity to do your job efficiently? Are you concerned that your job may be threatened because of a merger or because there are more talented people with whom you work?
7) Do you sometimes suspect that a supervisor or co-workers are conspiring or are biased against you?
8) Do you sometimes have a difficult time motivating yourself to go to work?
9) Do you lose your temper over trivial events at work?
10) Have you become more accident-prone?
11) Are you turning to drugs to deal with the problems at work? For example, do you find that you need extra coffee to get going in the morning? Or do you have to have a drink as soon as you get home from work?
12) Do you have headaches or other physical symptoms when you are at work?

If you answered yes to three or more of these questions, you are at risk for experiencing job burnout. If you answered yes to five or more of these questions, then the amount of job stress that you are experiencing probably is sufficient to impact on your future career and, even more seriously, on your physical and mental health.

Let's get specific. It is highly improbable that the entire job is stressful. Instead, it is more likely to be a specific aspect of the job. Use the following scoring system to narrow the problem down and then write the number in the space next to the category in the listing of specific sources of stress:

No problem/not applicable	**0**
Slight	**1**
Somewhat	**2**
Moderate	**4**
Exceeding	**6**
Overwhelming	**10**

Expectations at work
Requirements _____
Workload _____
Schedule _____
Compensation _____
Total Score _____

Infrastructure
Physical environment _____
Organizational climate _____
Politics _____
Total Score _____

Relationships
Superiors _____
Subordinates _____
Peers _____
Clients _____
Total score _____

The object of this exercise is to localize the major sources of your stress. Nothing else matters except for your perception of the events as being stressful. Irrespective of the appropriateness of your emotional and actual response, realize that your perception of events is all that counts. Note that the scoring system is not linear. Neither is the impact of stress upon your health.

Self-Evaluation

1. "Overall, I believe that my score is higher than others in my position, average, or lower."
   Why do you believe this?

2. "I experience the most stress with _____."
   Why do you think this is such a problem?

3. "I have the least stress with _____."
   Why?

In general, stressors arise from one of the following four categories:

❑ *Inevitable transitions:* Leaving home, marriage, having a child, etc.
❑ *Unexpected events:* Losing a job, divorce, accidents, etc.
❑ *Unrelenting conflict:* Incompatibility with spouse or co-workers, abuse, etc.
❑ *Personal:* Low self-esteem, unmet needs, chronic illness, etc.

As you contemplate the stressors in your life, ask, *"Why is this a problem for me?"* If the problem is overwhelming, start by dissecting it into its component parts. You will discover that while some solutions may lie beyond your control, others may have easy fixes.

WHAT IS STRESS?

During the 1970's and 1980's, there was a growing body of evidence supporting the existence of a powerful mind-body connection. An international gathering, hosted by the Belgian Royal Family, was convened in Brussels for the purpose of discussing the health ramifications of the emerging field called Psychoneuroimmunology. There was no disagreement that stress was a major factor, since there already was substantial literature documenting the links between emotional upheaval and illness. However, there was irreconcilable disagreement over how the word should be defined.

Should it be defined in chemical or psychological terms? Is it experienced in the same way by all people? How should it be measured? Is it the emotion or the response to the emotion that's the problem? Or perhaps the emotion is part of the response. "Are you afraid because you are running away, or are you running away because you are afraid?" is a question contemplated by the likes of Walter Canon and Claude Bernard, and which was now being paraphrased to accommodate a definition not of emotion, but rather the events associated with the expression of emotion. The discussion came to a sudden halt at the direction of the chairperson. He declared that it was a waste of time to continue, since it was apparent that consensus would not be reached in the allotted time. It was acknowledged that each person participating knew from personal experience and observation what stress was, and that each of us should embrace that understanding during the course of the subsequent discussions. We all agreed, pleased to have a quick way out of this intellectual quagmire. What does stress mean to you? In 2008, it meant impaired health to many Americans. The economic signs clearly indicated that not only the United

17

States, but the world was in the midst of an unprecedented financial crisis. And according to the American Psychological Association, 60 percent of Americans reported irritability or anger; 53 percent were fatigued; 52 percent had difficulty sleeping; and 48 percent engaged in unhealthy eating. These percentages were up substantially when compared with the 2007 findings. Of course, one size does not fit all. Chances are, if you feel distressed, yet you don't experience any of these widely reported symptoms, it's probably because you manifest stress in other ways. Here are some of the options:

Physical Symptoms Of Stress

Tension headaches
Frowning
Trembling of lips or
hands
Muscle tension
Neck aches
Back pain
Aggressive body language
Jaw pain
Increased sensitivity to
light and sound
Lightheadedness,
faintness, or dizziness
Ringing in the ears
Enlarged pupils
Blushing
Dry mouth
Problems swallowing
Frequent colds or bouts
with flu
Hives
Rashes
Chills or goose bumps

Heartburn
Stomach cramps
Nausea
Difficulty breathing
Restlessness
Trouble concentrating
Heart and chest pain
Increased perspiration
Night sweats
Cold, sweaty hands
Cold hands and feet
Flatulence or belching
Frequent urination
Constipation
Nervous diarrhea
Decreased sexual desire
Difficulty reaching
orgasm
Appetite change
Fatigue
Insomnia or hypersomnia
Weight change
Digestive upset

Pounding heart   Rapid heart beat
Shortness of breath   Autoimmune symptoms

Mental Symptoms Of Stress

Anxiety   Suicidal thoughts
Guilt   Fear of closeness to
Increased anger   people
Frustration   Loneliness
Moodiness   Dulled senses
Depression   Poor concentration
Nightmares   Low productivity
Trouble learning   Negative attitude
Forgetfulness   Defensiveness
Disorganization   Suspiciousness
Confusion   Whirling mind
Indecision   No new ideas
Feeling overwhelmed   Boredom
Discontentment   Spacing out

Behavioral Symptoms Of Stress

Inattention to grooming   Perfectionism
Increased tardiness   Reduced productivity
Serious appearance   Fast or mumbled speech
Unusual behavior   Unusual risk-taking
Nervous habits   Gritting of teeth
Rushing around or pacing   Lying
Increased alcohol use   Making excuses
Increased tobacco use   Social withdrawal
Gambling   Self-pity
Overspending   Strained communication
Edginess   Frustration
Overreaction   Mood swings
Prone to minor accidents   Bad temper

Crying spells	Easily discouraged
Stuttering	Procrastination
Nervous laughing	Nail-biting
Excessive worrying	

Undoubtedly, the word *stress* is one of the most misused words in the bio-medical sciences. It's used as a noun, a verb, as well as an adjective. Claude Bernard, a renowned physiologist, defined stress as "an adaptive response to an external stimulus." In other words, he defined the word *stress* as the changes which occur within the organism in response to some external signal. Walter Cannon, an equally renowned physiologist, defined stress as the stimulus. There is nothing wrong with either of these definitions. However, it is important to exercise caution in defining how the word is being used in a particular context. Physicists use the word *stressor* to describe the external event. For example, a stressor would be the force acting on an airplane wing or the suspension of a bridge. The word *strain* is used to describe the rearrangement of molecules within that structure. I will use *stressor* when referring to the triggering event and then, when appropriate, describe the specific chemical changes which are responsible for impairing your health.

General Adaptation Response: Even though there are many definitions, most people agree with the basic concepts that were put forward by Hans Selye when he described the general adaptation response. He described the stress response as being comprised of three phases. First, was the alarm or emergency phase, during which a person recognizes a potential threat to their well-being. Second, was the adaptation or resistance phase, during which chemical changes occur in order to allow you to return to a state of homeostasis or normalcy. This was followed by the exhaustion or illness phase, which Selye defined as the using up of the chemicals responsible for maintaining homeostasis. We now know the opposite is true. Problems arise from excessive production of stress-induced chemicals within the body – not their exhaustion.

Operational Definition Of Stress: A very practical definition of stress was put forward by Richard Lazarus when he stated, "It seems wise to use stress as a generic term for the whole area of problems that includes the stimuli producing stress reactions, the reactions themselves, and the various intervening processes. It defines a large, complex, amorphous, interdisciplinary area of interest and study." It is not a good definition because it is too broad. However, it does address all the important variables which you have to take into account when using the word *stress*. For example, everybody manifests a stress response. It may differ somewhat from one individual to another. Some people, when confronted with a major stressor, may experience a very rapid increase in heart rate, perhaps even to the point of experiencing tachycardia. For other individuals, their stomach might turn into knots with a major impact on their gastrointestinal system. Yet others may experience tension headaches or muscle tension. All these symptoms have a tendency to occur, but different individuals will have a predominance of one type of symptom or another. Furthermore, the type of response you have is the one you likely will manifest, regardless of the stressor. If your supervisor at work has just given you a letter informing you that your services are no longer needed just a couple of years before retirement, you are likely to experience a stress response. And whatever the type of response, it's the same one you will experience if you get cut off while driving down the interstate.

Types of Stress

Acute Versus Chronic Stress: *Acute stressors* are those which occur for a short period of time and, eventually, go away. That is precisely the type of stress with which the body has learned to deal. It is when the stressor persists over a long period of time that it is referred to as *chronic*, which is when health-related problems can arise.

Anabolism Versus Catabolism: If you took a course in Biochemistry when you were in high school or college, you might have spent an enormous amount of time studying enzymatic reactions, memorizing sequences of pathways, as well as examining chemical structures. Forget all of that. There are just two chemical reactions in the context of stress that are important. They are those dealing with *anabolism*, which is a fancy chemical term used to describe building processes, versus *catabolism*, which describes the breaking down of products. During the stress response, there is a shift from anabolic to catabolic processes, and the reason is quite logical. Why build for the future if there isn't going to be a future? For the same reason that you would not build a summer cottage on the seaside when a hurricane were bearing down on the lot, your body is not going to waste valuable time and resources on reproduction and other construction projects when the future is uncertain. In the short term, halting unessential building projects will not be harmful. For a period of days, even weeks, the changes are actually very beneficial. Problems occur when you switch from anabolic to catabolic processes over an extended period of months, or even years. That is when stress-related illness can result.

You also can view the stress response as a series of chemical reactions which are designed to provide energy: a process for extracting glucose and other energy substrates from storage. Glucose is not the only substrate. Other substrates might be needed as well, but glucose is one of the primary substrates, especially for the muscles and the central nervous system. However, converting glucose from stored energy sources and then putting what you didn't require back into storage is very wasteful. About 30 percent of the usable energy is lost, which is why many people under chronic stress suffer from fatigue.

This is so common that I have devoted an entire section to stress- related sleep and fatigue problems. But don't worry. There are several things you can do to energize yourself, no matter what is happening.

Somatic Versus Psychogenic Stress: There are many ways of categorizing the stress response. There are *somatic stressors,* which result in physical injury to the body. Chemical changes occur within the body, the tissue is repaired, and, eventually, unless damage is very severe, things will return to some sort of a homeostatic balance. It is the *psychogenic stressors* which cause problems. The anticipation of something that is perceived to be injurious to the body--even though it is not--can result in physiological changes. This is a bit misleading because a *somatic stressor* clearly will impact upon your psychological well-being, as well. Likewise, a *psychogenic stressor* will affect a number of nervous system pathways that are capable of impacting the body. Here is a listing of some of the potential ways you might respond when faced with uncertainty or threat.

Molecular Stress: Escaping your conscious awareness is the fact that a relentless stressor is at work, even as you breathe. It's estimated that between three to five percent of the oxygen you take in with each breath is converted into oxidative metabolites, which are more commonly referred to as free radicals.

Free radicals are unstable molecules, due to the fact that they are missing an electron. Like all things in nature, they seek stability by grabbing an electron from the most convenient source. This can be beneficial to your health when the electron is taken from a bacteria or virus. That's part of the mechanism whereby you rid yourself of an infection, and it is the reason why you need a certain number of free radicals in order to remain healthy. Problems arise when you have too many, through smoking, living in a polluted environment, or eating more than your fair share of fatty foods. Now, the extra free

23

radicals take the electrons from healthy cells. If that happens inside the blood vessel wall, it may give rise to arteriosclerosis. Or in the brain, it may contribute to Alzheimer's disease. Even some forms of cancer have been linked with excess free radicals. In addition, oxidative injury has been implicated in degenerative diseases, epilepsy, trauma, and stroke. It is a threshold phenomenon that occurs after antioxidant mechanisms are overwhelmed. Oxidative stress occurs when there's an imbalance between the rates of free radical production and their elimination.

Fortunately, there are a number of mechanisms within the body that serve to counter the damage done by free radicals. Antioxidant defenses include the enzymes superoxide dismutase, glutathione peroxidase, and catalase, as well as the low molecular weight reductants alpha-tocopherol (vitamin E), glutathione, and ascorbate (reduced vitamin C). This is why eating foods that are rich in these ingredients is such a healthy pursuit. There are many antioxidants available through the foods we eat. These include, amongst others, vitamins A, C, and E, which basically donate an electron, thereby sparing your healthy cells.

In a perfect world, you probably would get enough of these vitamins by eating a well-balanced diet. That doesn't always happen under stress. Chemicals in the brain prompt you to eat unhealthy proportions of carbohydrates, seek out fatty foods that make you feel good, and then store the excess fat in the abdominal region, where it has been correlated with cancer and heart disease. In addition, some people do not have the financial resources or time to eat in a healthy manner. That's why so many people turn to supplements that are rich in antioxidants, especially when they have reason to believe they have more than their fair share of these potentially harmful molecules.

HOW STRESS AFFECTS YOUR BODY

Stress impacts the body and mind through two primary mechanisms – the autonomic nervous system and the neuroendocrine pathways. Each will be discussed briefly to provide you with a better understanding of what is happening behind the biological scenes.

Autonomic Nervous System: During the course of a stress response, there are two primary circuits that become activated. One is the autonomic nervous system, and the other is referred to as the neuroendocrine circuit. The autonomic nervous system can be divided into two branches: the sympathetic and the parasympathetic. When you find yourself in a stressful situation, you might observe that your pupils begin to dilate. Salivation is stopped. You experience an increase in respiration and heartbeat. There is an inhibition of digestion and perhaps a relaxation of the bladder. Your body experiences an outpouring of catecholamines, epinephrine, and norepinephrine. These are all changes that are regulated by the sympathetic branch of the autonomic nervous system. The parasympathetic branch, however, is doing pretty much the opposite. For example, parasympathetic activation causes constriction of the pupils. It stimulates salivation, slows respiration and heart rate, and stimulates digestion.

Although it is not entirely correct, a general rule of thumb is those changes that occur as a result of sympathetic activation are those that are most often associated with the stress response. The parasympathetic reactions are those that normally are associated with the relaxation response.

Neuroendocrine Circuits: The other major conduit by which the brain is able to regulate various organs is the neuroendocrine circuits. When the stressful event is first perceived, it acts on neurons in the central nervous system, and from there the signals are transported to endocrine tissues,

25

hence *neuro-endocrine*. In the context of stress, the major circuit is the hypothalamic-pituitary-adrenal axis. The initial signal is corticotropin releasing factor, which is produced by neurons in the hypothalamus. This chemical makes its way through the blood stream to the pituitary gland, where it stimulates the release of two hormones. One is called adrenocorticotropin hormone, and the other is beta-endorphin. Adrenocorticotropin hormone travels through the body and makes its way to the adrenal gland, where it stimulates the release of cortisol. Cortisol is the major hormone produced in the wake of stress, and, because it is responsible for mobilizing glucose, is referred to as a glucocorticoid.

It is the release of endorphin that is primarily responsible for the reduction in pain sensitivity during stress. Many people, when they are in a car accident or have been wounded on a battlefield, do not realize the severity of their injuries until sometime later. The reason for this is because beta-endorphin, which means *endogenous morphine,* is released. It is a very potent painkiller, which makes sense. You don't want to be preoccupied with pain if you need to have your wits about you to extricate yourself from an emergency. You need to be able either to fight the threat or to escape from it, or as Walter Cannon described it, engage the *fight or flight response.*

Other changes may occur as well, depending upon the type of stress. Some people may have a release of growth hormone and prolactin. There also are interactions between the stress circuits and the reproductive axes. For example, corticotropin releasing factor and beta-endorphin both are capable of suppressing reproductive hormones, which is one of the reasons why amenorrhea is a common symptom in women under chronic stress and why impotence is not an uncommon symptom in men. This all makes sense. If you are living with chronic stress, one of the last things you need to be bothered with is raising offspring.

Growing Through Crisis And Change: Crisis and change, capable of giving rise to stress, are a part of life. Indeed, they are a necessary part of life, providing the motivation to grow. There really is no way to grow without dealing with life's difficulties and changes. You have the basic choice of learning and growing through the difficult times or more rigidly adhering to your familiar ways of doing things. The key is learning to accept that life is difficult, but trusting that you have the resources to make it through the tough times. Times of crisis and change can be viewed as threats or as challenges. It really depends on how you choose to view them.

Your resilience or ability to adapt to change often centers on your self-esteem. If you see yourself as powerless or unworthy, change can be very threatening, and you may fear not being able to deal with the changes. That is when an inner sense of worth is important. When you have come to trust your inner worth, the changes and tough times in life are less unsettling because you know you can rely on your inner resources. If you don't have a solid sense of who you are, you may adopt a rigid approach to life that freezes you in time, making it less likely that you will cope effectively when challenged by life's difficulties. As you feel more confident in yourself, you simultaneously feel safer and better equipped to deal with the challenges in life, whether it be death, the loss of a job, a move, or a divorce.

Most difficulties in life involve losses, and, as such, your response to them often depends on how you have dealt with past losses. If losses in the past have overwhelmed your ability to cope or simply come too soon or too fast, loss may terrify you. Often a new loss will confront you with your past experiences with loss and lead to feelings of powerlessness or helplessness. It is the experience of loss that all of us must deal with at many points in life. Most changes involve something lost and something gained. If you lose sight of what is gained

27

and focus only on the loss, the prospect of change invariably will evoke fear.

Many events can throw you off course in life. If your feet are firmly planted on the ground - that is, you value yourself as a person, feel in your heart that basically you are a good person, and have a sense of stability - it is less likely that you will get swept away by life's challenges. This isn't to say you won't be distressed at times -- fear is a normal reaction to change. In the right proportion, it is fear that prepares us to cope better. To deal with crisis and change in life, it is important to look inward to work on ways of taking care of yourself with the support of people who are close to you, accepting the cycle of loss. In this way, you can keep pace with change. By looking for the "opportunities within the crisis," you can begin to grow through them.

EMOTIONS

Scientists, philosophers, and artists have never been able to reach agreement on the true definition of emotions. What has been agreed upon, at least within the scientific community, is that there are generally six recognized families of emotion:

- ❑ Anger
- ❑ Disgust
- ❑ Fear
- ❑ Joy
- ❑ Love
- ❑ Sadness

Some would argue that this list needs to be expanded to include shame and guilt. However, I would regard these as subcategories of fear: fear of social rejection or of punishment. Likewise, rage and adoration are degrees of anger and love respectively, although some people might consider them as separate emotions.

Tune Into Your Feelings: It is very important that you understand why you are responding in the manner that you are. Too often, you respond only to the emotion. Or, you might focus upon only your behavioral response or the social consequences. Before you can modify your response, you first must identify it to gain an understanding of why it is occurring. Ultimately, realize that the purpose of stress-induced emotions and behavior is to provide balance. The experience of emotions helps you either to reduce the sadness, to eliminate the trigger of disgust, or to counter the threat.

Consider a symphony orchestra in performance before an attentive audience. I will use the orchestra to represent the mind and the audience to represent the body. The musicians are the brain cells, while the notes they play are the chemicals which now will affect the body.

When the orchestra performs synchronically and in harmony, its effect upon the audience (the body) will be the desired interpretation of the music. The strains of a gentle *etude* induce relaxation, while *The 1812 Overture* will elicit arousal, and the intentional, intermittent discordance of *The Rite of Spring* might elevate such arousal to a level of discomfort for some.

Yet, the audience also plays a role in the workings of the performance. Under optimal circumstances, it responds in balance with the effort of the orchestra. But the actions of individuals strongly can impact the rest of the audience as well as the performers themselves. There is a woman seated nearby who repeatedly snaps her purse open and shut as she consumes candy wrapped in extremely crinkly paper. This distraction significantly interferes with the ability of those around her to concentrate fully on the music. A man in the audience suffers from a hacking cough and sneezes loudly. Those nearby must contend with the distraction of the noise as well as that of being exposed to the man's illness. Instead of remaining in synch with the music, their attention is diverted. Furthermore, members of both the audience and the orchestra may be distracted by emotions associated with recent events in their personal lives, such as the second violinist who's concerned her contract won't be renewed and has no idea that the head cold she currently suffers from took hold because she's run down from worry.

Every element of the performance's outcome, for both orchestra and audience, is interwoven. While extremely simplified, it is analogous with the subtle interaction which constantly occurs between your mind and body. By understanding the impact of external and internal events, and, to a great degree, learning to control the stressors influencing them, you can better orchestrate your own health and well-being.

❑ Emotions are more than 'all in your head' as biological pathways link the brain and the body.
❑ Emotions can arise as a result of real or perceived events.
❑ Genetics and early life experiences play a role in shaping your emotions.
❑ The body can be trained to experience particular emotional and physical responses to events.

Emotions play a very important role in modulating the balance between good health and disease. When you can freely access emotions, you can experience the richness and passion of life, be it pleasure or pain. Some people are under the impression that they can somehow block out only the painful emotions, while preserving the more pleasurable ones. Normally, when you block emotions, you block them all, both pleasurable and painful. Feelings of numbness and depression can be signs that you tend to block your emotions.

A highly effective way of coping with stress is to deal directly with emotions. First, pay attention to how you may distract yourself from your feelings. Do you do any of the following?

• Keep busy?
• Watch too much TV?
• Reach for something to eat or drink?
• Sleep too much?
• Intellectualize?
• Focus on other people?
• Engage in excessive shopping?

Whichever your preferred method, interrupt the process by stopping and spending five or ten minutes of quiet time to focus on what you are feeling. If you are not used to dealing with emotions, you may find it helpful to focus on your body and determine which of the following emotions you are experiencing: anger, sadness, or fear. In some instances, you will be feeling a combination of these. Try not to judge or filter the emotions--simply let them come up to the surface. Then stay with the emotion for longer periods of time. Just *let* it happen, don't try to *make* it happen, and do not confuse thinking about emotions with feeling emotions. These are entirely different processes. Feeling is a freeing, spontaneous experience which, unlike conscious thought, cannot be forced.

Getting To Know Me: Your responses to stress are shaped by your thoughts and feelings. As you develop a greater awareness, you will begin to realize that your thoughts and feelings about stressful events are not automatic, but, at some level, involve a choice. The key is to be aware of this and make a choice to engage in a different thought process.

Build your confidence by thinking of a time in your life when you made a decision to do something. A time when you were committed to a particular course of action and believed, without a doubt, that you could accomplish your goal. A time when you were determined. Imagine how you felt at that time. If you cannot think of a decision you made, imagine something that you strongly believe in with no reservations. Then, imagine feeling as committed to changing your unhealthy patterns of behavior. Now create this same feeling of conviction with respect to changing your response to stressful events.

After you have taken some time to identify the patterns of dealing with stress that you wish to change, and have reinforced your commitment to actually making these changes, you can now begin to focus specifically on making changes.

Stress can be broken down into three parts: the trigger, the interpretation, and the resulting emotion. The trigger is the external event that you are dealing with; the interpretation is how you size it up; and the emotion is what follows. Of course, all of these components affect each other. You can change your stress response by directly focusing on one of these three components. The easiest place to focus is on the triggers. Then fill in the rest of the following table.

Personal Stressors		
Trigger	Interpretation	Emotion
Supervisor	*Unrealistic demands*	*Anger*

- *What conclusions can you draw about the situations that are particularly difficult for you?*
- *Are they ones that you could avoid?*
- *Are you distressed because particular people in your life are critical of you or question your judgment?*
- *Are there people in your life you can never please?*
- *Do you find your job leaves you feeling unhappy and unfulfilled?*

If these are some of the triggers, it might be possible to make some direct changes to eliminate or reduce them. You are the only one who can decide whether they are so unhealthy and damaging to your health that you should make some major changes in your life, or whether they are necessary evils that you cannot avoid and which you must learn to deal with. Alternatively, it may be your interpretation of events that is in need of change.

Just My Style

Do you fit into one of the following categories?

> **Apprehensive**
> - What if something happens to me?
> - What if I can't finish it?
> - What if I lose control?

These are the typical thoughts of the apprehensive person. Their favorite statement is "what if" as they constantly anticipate the worst case scenario and create exaggerated images of failure. This type of person will be in a constant state of stress while engaging in this process.

> **Failure**
> - Why am I so clumsy?
> - Why can't I get it right?
> - Why didn't I do it that way?

Listen for the word 'why,' and chances are you have identified a person who considers himself to be a failure. He compares himself with others, and he constantly focuses upon weaknesses instead of strengths. This individual is unlikely ever to achieve high self-esteem or success.

> **Casualty**
> - I can't do that, so why bother trying?
> - I'm too uncoordinated to attempt that.
> - It won't make any difference.

Unfortunately, the real obstacle preventing a 'casualty' from achieving his objective is a pessimistic attitude. He always will find an obstacle and, invariably, will blame circumstances outside himself. In other words, there's nothing he can do. The result? Flight, often leading to a constant feeling of helplessness and depression.

Intolerant
- You must do it this way.
- This has to be done again.
- I should always be perfect.

Such a person often sets unrealistic goals and then considers himself to be a failure if he does not accomplish his objective. He is a perfectionist and intolerant of failure. You'll often hear the word 'must' in such a person's dialogues.

Changing Unhealthy Thoughts

Do you see yourself in one or more of the previous categories? If yes, ask yourself the following questions:

- "Will I accomplish anything worthwhile by continuing this process?"
- "Do I want to continue feeling the way I do?"
- "Are these thoughts justified?"

Now, write down each negative thought and answer the following questions.

- "What are the chances the scenario I am preoccupied with will really unfold?"
- "Is what I am thinking always true, or just sometimes?
- "If I do this, what is the worst that could happen?"

- "If the worst case scenario does occur, will it really be that bad? What would my options be?"
- "Am I considering all the information available to me?"
- "Am I considering all the information with equal importance, or am I twisting facts to fit my preconceived notions?"
- "What is the evidence my thoughts are justified?"

Next, replace each negative thought with a positive one.

For example, "I'll never be able to do this" can become, "If I take time to learn this particular skill, I will be able to do this."

Or, "I'll be useless tomorrow if I don't fall asleep soon" can become, "Even lying in bed awake is a form of rest. I've functioned before with minimal sleep; I can do it again." As you replace the negative thoughts with positive ones, remember the following simple rules:

- ❏ Avoid using words with negative connotations.
- ❏ Stay in the present.
- ❏ Use the personal pronoun whenever you can.

Remember that your response to any event will be triggered by the image you create in your mind. That image will be shaped by your biases, your expectations, and your past experiences. They may be hard to rearrange. There's an old Chinese proverb:

> *"What your eyes see and your ears hear is what is already in your mind."*

In addition to changing your thoughts, you also can work to change your emotions.

❑ If you feel sad, frightened, or defeated, the first step is to acknowledge it rather than make it go away. Then you can begin to change the feeling.

❑ If you are frightened or overwhelmed, focus on a time in your life when you felt safe or in control. Focus on how it feels to be safe or in control.

❑ Imagine you can make this feeling of being in control ten percent stronger, then twenty percent stronger, then fifty percent stronger. Repeat this process throughout the day. Soon you will find that you can change your emotional response to events.

In those circumstances that are clearly out of your control, there are other approaches you can use. First, it is sometimes very helpful simply to accept the fact that the situation is out of your hands. Let it go. People tend to labor over how to control a situation out of their control, which just makes them more upset. When you begin to feel anxious or distressed, that is when it is probably time to simply set it aside for a while and come back to it later.

Another approach is to focus on the piece you can control. In some cases, the only thing you really can control is your attitude. Some people surrender their sense of personal control by believing other people always must approve of their actions, or that they never can make mistakes, or that they never can be vulnerable. These mindsets or beliefs insure that you will have little control over major aspects of your life. By changing these expectations or beliefs and by developing inner strength, you will find that you are faced with fewer out of control situations in life.

What types of beliefs do you maintain that keep you feeling unhappy and powerless? Be aware of how these beliefs operate in your life, and confront them when they occur.

Many people make the mistake of defining their goal in unrealistic ways, or else they confuse a reward for having achieved a goal with the actual goal. I once spoke at a large convention attended by several thousand entrepreneurs, who were being worked into a frenzy by their successful colleagues. Each began by describing the Mercedes or yacht now parked at their multi-million dollar mansion. Then, the eager attendees were instructed to cut out pictures of Rolex watches, their dream car, or other expensive possessions and place them in highly visible locations around the house. The idea was to be constantly reminded of their goal and of what life would be like when it was achieved. But the car or mansion morphed into the goal, when it should have been viewed as the reward. If a goal is truly worthwhile, the rewards will come automatically. By taking their sight off their goal, they were more likely missing their opportunities.

Goals should be things such as building a flourishing business, exceeding your sales quota, or paying off your debt. A goal must be defined in ways that easily can be measured, and in a manner that can be charted along the way. Think about it. That car is all or nothing. You don't acquire small pieces as you make progress. A correctly defined goal will enable you to identify progress each and every day. And one more thing. Make sure that you have defined a goal in a manner that you have control over.

What Are Your Values And Beliefs? Having goals that are inconsistent with your values will be a constant source of conflict. What are your primary values?

Refer to the following list; subtract from it or add to it if what you value is not listed. Create a personal list beginning with the values that are most important to you, and then determine if they are compatible with your goals.

Values	
Wealth	Material possessions
Love	Friendship
Power	Career
Altruism	Family
Labor	Higher power

In addition to identifying your goals and values, you also need to identify your belief system. How would you complete these statements?

- Life is _____.

- People are_____.

- Stress is _____.

- Relationships are_____.

- The world would be a better place to live if_____.

- I am_____.

And now ask yourself:

- Are these your beliefs or those of someone else?

- Are your beliefs based upon consistent experience?

- Can you think of times in your life when your belief system was challenged by reality?

- Have beliefs ever kept you from achieving a goal?

- Are certain themes reflected in your beliefs?

- Are you willing to change one or more of your beliefs if they are obstacles to your goals?

Now that you have pondered these questions, make a list of those beliefs that are most dear to you, making sure that they are rational and yours. Then, re-examine your goals, making certain that there are no conflicts between your beliefs and your long-term objectives.

Plan Of Action

Write down your goals. Remember to use positive statements, be realistic, and establish a timetable.

- My goal is to _____.

- The following are potential obstacles that might interfere with my achieving my goal._____.

- I am willing to take the following steps to minimize the effects of these obstacles. _____.

- By _____, I will be halfway to having completed my goal. By _____, I will have achieved it.

Be prepared to modify these dates. The unexpected will occur, and you need to make allowances. You might consider giving yourself more time than you think you really need. This way, you won't be disappointed by failing to meet a deadline; and if you reach the milestone sooner than projected, relish your triumph.

Helpful Hints

- **Ritualize** your behavior by setting aside a time of day when you take steps to achieve your goal. Make sure you do something each day so that through conditioning, the clock will become a gentle reminder.

- **Remain** focused on the objective. If it seems overwhelming at times, then divide the task into manageable steps. Remember, a journey is completed one small step at a time.

- **Restate** your goal, taking into account shifting priorities and unexpected changes in your life.

- **Redefine** the objective as a challenge.

- **Resolve** to stay the course, and, if you deviate, remind yourself about the benefits of accomplishing your objective.

- **Reward** yourself as you make quantifiable progress toward your goal.

Organize Your Life: Most people underestimate the time that is required to complete a task. A study of undergraduate students conducted by Roger Buehler of Simon Frazer University has revealed that estimates are off by almost three weeks for long term projects. The problem is what is referred to as an *optimistic bias*. People tend to focus primarily upon their future plans and pay very little attention to relevant experience. Furthermore, people tend to ignore the obstacles that prevented them from completing a similar task on time in the past and blindly assign unrealistic deadlines. Here's what you can do.

❑ How you handle the optimistic bias depends upon what the consequences of underestimation might be. If missing a deadline is going to place you in a lot of hot water, then you might want to get some input from someone who knows not only about your past performance but about your future plans as well. Chances are your boss meets those criteria. It's interesting that studies have shown that while people often will underestimate their own completion dates, they generally will overestimate the finish times of others. So, if you want to get the most accurate time of completion, take into account your estimate and your boss' estimate, which probably will be overly conservative, and then split the difference.

❑ When a supervisor is not available, then you have to mull over your own track record and identify the rate-limiting steps that will prevent you from completing the task. For example, if you have to rely upon input from a co-worker who is often unavailable, then that has to be factored in.

❑ If there will be no consequences for missing the target date, then there's no point in being optimistic about the completion time. The bottom line is that if missing a deadline is going to spell trouble, then consider your past experiences. If there will not be consequences, then just plow on with the project.

A major cause of burnout in the work place as well as in your personal endeavors is failure to achieve goals. Many books have been written on the subject about how to manage your time, and there are numerous seminars that are offered to help you get motivated. In general, the advice is basically the same. You need to have a general idea of what it is that needs to be accomplished in defined units of time, and then you need to set priorities. It also is a good idea to apply some of the same goal-achieving behaviors that you use in the work setting in your personal life, as well.

Everyone ought to have objectives that they want to achieve in order to provide some purpose to their lives. And whatever dream that happens to be, it should be realistic, and it should be something that you want, and not something that you are doing to please other people. Did you know that just thinking about a goal or writing that goal down will facilitate your accomplishing it? Once you've identified what it is you want to achieve, it becomes easier to identify information and circumstances that you can use to help you achieve that goal. From this point on, though, you need to be careful.

Keep in mind that I did not write this book. I wrote sentences, which came together as paragraphs, which then became chapters. If I had set about to write a book, I doubt I would have even started. Finding the time to take on such a project would have been daunting. But finding time to research a topic, and then knocking out a few paragraphs was never a problem. Do the same thing. Divide your ultimate goal into its component parts. As each part is completed, you will feel successful, which will make you act successful, and, before you know it, you're there.

Don't Worry; Be Happy: There are some people who can't seem to help worrying. About 30 percent of us are non-worriers, 15 percent are chronic worriers, and the rest fall somewhere in between. If you happen to be a chronic worrier, and you have tried everything you can to change, at least work to gain some control over your worrying behavior. After all, it's not how much you worry, but whether your worrying is interfering with your ability to function. Is it distracting you, keeping you from engaging in work or performing well in school? Is it causing you to lose sleep? One way to gain control over your worrying is to simply set aside a period of time when you are going to worry.

Select a time when worrying is least likely to be disruptive. It should be a period that is going to last about 30 minutes. Less or more time actually may intensify your worrying. Be careful where you do it. Don't sit in your favorite chair. Don't lie in bed worrying. Otherwise, you will turn the bedroom or your favorite location into reminders that later will evoke the same worrying behavior.

The objective of setting aside periods of time to worry is to break the worry cycle and to keep it from interfering with other activities. It's based on the principle of habituation. Think for a moment about your favorite meal. If you were to eat that food for breakfast, lunch, and dinner, chances are you wouldn't be able to stand even being in the same kitchen where it was being prepared after a few days. In very much the same way, setting aside periods of time during the day when you are going to worry, will enable you to habituate yourself. By designating time in the day when that's all you are going to do, it decreases the probability that the worrying will interfere with what you really need to be getting on with in your life. In short, take control over your worrying.

Stop Thinking About It: There's a significant difference between choosing to let something go and avoiding it. *Choosing* puts you in control, while evading the subject lets the problem have control over you.

When you're faced with a conflict, ask yourself this simple question: "Is there anything I can do right now about this problem that I have not already done?"

If there is, then do it. Take some type of appropriate action immediately. Then once you have taken action, set the matter aside. If there is nothing else you can do, then let it go. Ruminating or obsessing about events rarely leads to any real solutions. Some of us are afraid to let go because of the belief that we are somehow working on the problem by worrying about it. Remember the wisdom of Reinhold Niebuhr:

"God, grant me the serenity to accept the things I cannot change, courage to change the things I can, and wisdom to know the difference."

- ❑ Many of your worries are related to past events you can no longer control.
- ❑ Most of the rest are related to what may occur in the future, of which at least half won't happen.
- ❑ Focus your resources on today. That's what you are most likely to have control over.

Resolve Situations As They Arise: The ability to rapidly resolve conflicts reflects a healthy state of mind. Anxiety and feelings of sadness or depression are sometimes the product of unresolved conflicts. The emotional residue of each circumstance may be stored and may interfere with feelings of contentment and peace. It is easy to carry around these unresolved feelings and become fatigued and burdened by them. The more effectively you resolve situations as they arise, the more effectively you can live in the present and be unencumbered by the past. Patterns of resolving or not resolving conflict are often a function of early experiences, particularly very traumatic experiences. To resolve particularly difficult conflicts may require professional assistance.

Ask Yourself:

- Do I tend to resolve situations as they arise?

- Do I find myself regretting not having said important things to people during past episodes of my life?

- Do I tend to 'smooth over' conflict when it occurs in relationships?

- Do I avoid conflict at all costs?

- Is it difficult for me to express emotions?

- Do I tend to rehash the events in my life, or, perhaps, preview possible solutions over and over in my mind, but never progress to the point where I take concrete action?

Take a moment to focus on how you feel when you avoid dealing with important situations. Focus on an image in the past week when you know you would have been better off to have brought something up that was bothering you, or when you regretted leaving something undone that you would have preferred to do. Let this feeling serve as a cue to practice resolving conflicts in the present. Stop and think of what you can say or do to reach some resolution, if only on a temporary basis. It may simply involve saying to someone, *"Hey, I would like to talk about what just happened; do you have some time tomorrow?"* Do something; do anything. Otherwise, you will reinforce your feelings of helplessness.

Resolving situations as they arise will probably confront you with your fears of failure or shame. People often avoid dealing with conflict because they do not believe their actions will be effective, or they are worried that others will respond negatively towards them. Ironically, avoiding conflict often sabotages relationships and makes life even more difficult. Soon, you actually do become ineffective, and, as a result, people no longer respond to you in a positive way. It becomes a self-fulfilling prophecy. This does not mean that it is best for you to analyze or to talk about every minor difficulty; it does mean that you take every step to resolve uncomfortable feelings as they arise in your life by either resolving your own inner feelings or by taking some concrete action.

Remember:

- You always have choices. If nothing else, you can choose your attitude.
- You always will act in accordance with your beliefs.
- Your stress decreases as your sense of control and optimism increases.

Get It Off Your Chest: Writing about the experiences in your life can be quite an effective strategy for reaching resolution and expressing emotions. Writing is simple and can be done almost anywhere, anytime. There is something about putting your thoughts and feelings on paper that helps. Sometimes, it simply helps you to break the cycle of ruminating about the event. Other times, it helps you to express important emotions. Or, it may help you to organize your feelings. Regardless, you will be surprised at the effectiveness of this technique.

The first step is to set aside fifteen or twenty minutes each day to write. Choose a time when you can be alone with your thoughts and feelings, free from distractions. Find a place and a time to do this each day and do it consistently. Simply write whatever comes to mind. You might focus on the events of the day or on an ongoing problem; you might reflect on a difficult event during your childhood, or you might write about a very happy experience in your life. Do not censor what you write: just write. In essence, you will be practicing *free association*. You write whatever comes to mind. If you find this hard to do, imagine writing to a friend, one you know very well. Tell her everything about your day, everything about your life, everything about yourself. Write about your joy, your fear, your anger, or your pain.

Talk Things Out With Yourself: There are many times in life when you may feel pressured to make a decision. Few decisions in life come without some degree of doubt, and conflict is a part of life. Dialogues, in written or spoken form, are useful in resolving these conflicts. Basically, this technique involves letting yourself experience two opposite sides of a conflict or quandary, like taking both sides in a debate. Imagine two opposing personalities or voices. Each personality gets the opportunity to discuss fully their side of the argument or their reason for making a particular choice, and the other gets to respond. This technique gives words to emotions, allowing feelings to be expressed and alternatives to be explored. You probably will feel silly at first, but give this exercise a fair chance. It really does work.

The sharing of feelings has proven to be highly therapeutic, leading to long-term gains in well-being. Under controlled conditions, undergraduate college students were asked to recall verbally the most traumatic event in their lives. One group narrated only the factual occurrences of the event, with no mention of their feelings about it. A second group described both the event and their feelings. A control group was asked to simply state what they were wearing or some other circumstantial element that had no emotional connotation. Those people who recalled their feelings about the events experienced an initial episode of increased anxiety as well as a decline in their immune systems. But over the course of the semester, it was the members of this group whose immune systems became more robust, resulting in fewer visits to the student health center. There was something about the act of disclosure that was both emotionally therapeutic and had an impact upon the immune system's ability to rebound.

How Disclosure Of Emotions Works: Several explanations have been offered. Among the most plausible is that when speaking or writing about a problem, you are forced to slow down. Information which has been ricocheting around the emotional brain is delayed during its translation into language. Your thoughts become organized. The problem is then perceived through different sensory pathways – through your eyes in the case of written disclosure, through your ears in the case of verbal disclosure. Each form of processing also takes time, adding a third modality, and it requires physical movement, adding a fourth. As a result, your mind often finds it easier to recognize potential solutions to improve or to overcome the perceived difficulty.

Desensitization is another hypothesis. Through the repetitive act of expressing your feelings, the emotional edge eventually wears off. Like watching re-runs of the same television program over and over again, you become tired of rehashing the same feelings and are able to distance yourself from their impact. (But this can also have the potential result of re-traumatizing a person, depending on the setting and the reception s/he receives.)

- Language provides a means of emotional expression.
- Language allows you to express your emotions in a controllable format.
- Putting your emotions into words allows you to perceive them from a new perspective.

50

❑ Simply changing the words you use can alter your emotional response to past or present events.

Some people have a difficult time disclosing emotion. Divulging your feelings is, in a sense, counter to being in control. You have a tendency to feel vulnerable. Furthermore, the longer a feeling has been suppressed, the more likely it is to emerge with a vengeance. By virtue of differences in temperament or early learning experiences, some people have difficulty accessing their emotions. In some cases, this stems from a fear of not being in control, or from a resistance to feel pain. You may have experienced an extraordinarily painful experience early in life and were so overwhelmed by the feeling that you learned to shut down the emotions whenever they began to surface. Write down those feelings you experienced in association with a recent stressor.

Language is both expressive of emotion, and it is a means through which emotion is expressed. Through the use of words, your expressing your feelings is extremely beneficial to both your mental and physical well-being. Maladies in many forms can arise when emotions constantly are repressed. It may seem that by ignoring your feelings, you are maintaining control over them, but actually the opposite, eventually, becomes true. The buried emotions find other ways to make themselves known. It may be through recurrent nightmares for the adult who believes he or she is over the sexual abuse that occurred in childhood. Anger, when turned inwards, eventually may manifest itself as a heart attack. In one way or another, your emotions will demand to be acknowledged. Why not do it on your terms and make emotions work for, instead of against, you?

SOCIAL SUPPORT

Loneliness is a major risk factor for disease. Indeed, it is suspected that one of the reason's people who believe in voodoo die after they learn a curse has been placed upon them is because they are shunned when the news spreads. Human contact is not only pleasurable; it is one of the most effective buffers against stress available to you.

❏ Associating with other living things produces beneficial emotional and physical results.
❏ Family, friends, pets, and plants provide emotional benefits by connecting you to the world outside yourself.
❏ Caring for others provides you with a sense of control over events.
❏ The behaviors associated with caring for people, pets, or plants reinforce a responsibility for your own well-being.

Assessing Your Social Safety Net:

Answer the following questions as true or false:
1. If I needed an emergency loan of $100, there is someone from whom I could get it.
2. There is someone who takes pride in my accomplishments.
3. I often meet or talk with family or friends.
4. Most people I know think highly of me.

Add up the number of true answers you recorded to these first four questions. Now continue.
5. If I needed an early morning ride to the airport, there's no one I would feel comfortable asking to take me.
6. I feel there is no one with whom I can share my most private worries and fears.

7. Most of my friends are more successful in making changes in their lives than I am.
8. I would have a hard time finding someone to go with me on a day trip to the beach or to the country.

Add up the number of times you responded with 'false' to the last four questions. And now add the number of 'true' responses to the first four questions to the number of 'false' responses to the second four. If your score is three or less, then you probably have inadequate social support. If it's four or more, then you likely have a good social safety net.

Barriers To Friendship: Some people create personal barriers to meaningful relationships. Because of unhealthy beliefs, they go to great lengths to avoid contact with others, although not in all circumstances. You may be outgoing in the workplace, where your role in the hierarchy is well defined, but you may feel ill at ease at a party. If there ever are circumstances under which you have difficulty communicating with others, it may be due to one of the following beliefs:

I don't want to appear silly or intrusive.
I'm concerned about sexual overtones.
I feel unworthy to be speaking to that person.

Respond to each that applies, as well as to others with which you identify, by asking the same questions that you would use to probe other beliefs:

❑ Are these your beliefs or those of someone else?
❑ Are your beliefs based upon experience?
❑ Can you think of times in your life when your belief system was challenged by reality?
❑ Have your beliefs ever kept you from achieving a goal?
❑ Are certain themes reflected in your beliefs?
❑ Are you willing to change one or more of your beliefs if they are obstacles to your goals

When you make contact with others, let them know what you need from them. Some people intuitively will know how to support you; others will not. Some people will try to give advice; some people will talk about their own problems; others will try to cheer you up. While these responses can be helpful, it is better to talk with someone who knows how to listen.

Usually, what you need most when distressed is someone who can listen without judging. They don't have to solve your problem; they simply are there to hear you out. This provides you with an opportunity to express your thoughts and emotions, something that is extremely important when you are feeling distressed. If you don't have a partner, a family member, or a friend who can do this, you might want to talk with a professional therapist. The key is talking with someone who will allow you to express your feelings.

Remember to reciprocate. No one is devoid of hardship. Become a resource for those upon whom you depend. The following guidelines will greatly enhance your listening skills:

- ❏ Focus upon the other person's words and body language.
- ❏ Show interest by raising your eyebrows in response to what is being said.
- ❏ Use facial gestures, such as a smile, to convey empathy.
- ❏ Seek clarification when appropriate.
- ❏ Summarize.

DEALING WITH BURNOUT

Burnout is due to the cumulative effect of stress. It most often occurs in the workplace or home setting. While each situation requires a customized approach for dealing with it, there are some general guidelines that work for most people:

- ❑ **Set Priorities:** Insufficient time to complete tasks is a major contributor to stress and burnout. You have to set priorities. You can't do everything, so you have to determine those things that absolutely must be done first. And write them down on a piece of paper - one of those little sticky notes works well. When you complete the task, either check it off or crumple up the piece of paper and throw it away. Each of those strategies gives you a feeling of accomplishment.

- ❑ **Learn To Set Limits:** It's important to learn to say 'no' when you might be asked to engage in some behavior that you know in advance is going to cause you some distress. A lot of people make the mistake of saying yes when they really want to say no. Learning how to say no is perhaps one of the most important steps in dealing with stress, whether it is occurring in your personal life or whether it's occurring in your professional environment. If you say yes too often, you also rob yourself of precious recovery time.

- ❑ **Seek Advice:** Don't be afraid to ask questions. Seek out advice from your co-workers or people who might have more experience dealing with a particular problem that you have.

Remember, you are allowed to share your problems with people and to talk things out.

❑ **Delegate:** You need to delegate responsibility and not believe you have to be the one who has to carry the full weight of the problem on your shoulders. No one can handle everything.

❑ **Set Realistic Goals:** You have to be realistic about meeting objectives. There are certain things that just can't be done with the resources available to you or completed within a given deadline.

Put On A Happy Face: For several years, I was engaged in research attempting to find out if people can use acting skills as a means by which to change their personalities. The study came about as a result of an observation I made many years earlier of a person who had been diagnosed with Multiple Personality Disorder, now referred to as Dissociative Identity Disorder. This is a rare condition where several distinct personalities, each residing within the same body, are exhibited. An experiment was designed where a small amount of blood was drawn before and after each personality exhibited itself. Profound changes were observed in the number of cells in the immune system after certain types of personalities had been expressed.

This led to a study designed to determine if a mentally healthy person could 'act' like a particular personality and elicit changes in his or her physiology. Two actors were chosen to play contrasting roles (one very negative and depressing, the other uplifting) in a 30-minute scene. After a brief intermission, a second 30-minute play was performed, and the actors switched roles. The program was presented nightly for two weeks before live audiences. Before and after each of the performances, blood samples were drawn from both the actors and the audience members. My research team was amazed to note that several changes occurred in the immune system, which were consistent with observations reported in the medical literature, indicating that depression was correlated with impaired immunity. In short, by simply acting in a depressed way, certain measures of the immune system are decreased.

Many people, when they hear the word *acting*, think automatically of *faking it*. I use the word *acting* to describe a process whereby a person elicits a true emotion in order to achieve a particular physiological response - acting like a winner to become a winner. The signals transmitted to this person's brain are very similar to those that would be transmitted if that person were experiencing the same emotion in response to something occurring within his environment. The emotion this person elicits through acting is a true emotion.

It's easy to observe such emotional alternation within ourselves. First, put a deep frown on your face, and count to ten. Now, observe how you feel, both physically and mentally. Next, move your facial muscles into the form of a smile. Again, count to ten, and observe the changes experienced in both your mind and body. Try it.

The way you behave can contribute to the severity of symptoms that you might experience in illness. By employing acting skills, you may be able to modify your body in ways that will decrease the probability of becoming ill.

> ❏ Acting using a particular emotion can fool the body into experiencing the physiological changes that occur when actually experiencing that emotion.

❑ Negative emotions suppress the immune system, which can lead to physical and mental illnesses.

Whenever I Feel Afraid, I Hold My Head Erect: Problems arise when an emotion is expressed inappropriately. This can include unleashing an emotional response at the wrong target or when emotional expression interferes with your ability to perform.

When you assume a certain body posture, feedback signals are transmitted back into your body, eliciting a physiological state to match what is on the surface. So, basically, wearing a mask of confidence elicits a state of confidence. Use these body language tips to perform more effectively:

- Stand or sit with your back straight.
- Hold your shoulders back.
- Relax your arms and hands.
- Lift your chin.
- Focus your eyes on the person with whom you're dealing.
- Hold this pose - even a brief lapse can be sufficient to cause you to lose your confidence.

Your physical stance can impact your emotional response to stressful events. If the situation involves another person, your body language also can impact their emotional responses.

Bottom Line

❑ You always have choices. If nothing else, you can choose your attitude.

❑ You always will act in accordance with your beliefs.

❑ Your stress decreases as your sense of control and optimism increases.

If We Couldn't Laugh, We Would All Go Insane: There is nothing more effective to reduce blood pressure and relax muscles than having a good laugh. It may stimulate endorphin release within the brain, which would certainly explain the feeling of well-being that is associated with humor; but, at the very least, it's a brief diversion from the stressors in your life.

How is it that some people are able to relate the most dreadful experiences in such a way that they and everyone around them dissolve into spasms of laughter? When telling of their home being destroyed by a fire, they focus on the scent of barbecued beef wafting up from the freezer after it exploded. Or they can aptly recall the children's bath toys floating off in a flotilla after the flood. It certainly isn't that they are immune to devastation and loss or the incredible problems they face in putting their lives back together. Instead, they understand, even subconsciously, that how they choose to perceive the problem, whether through weirdness or woe, has an impact upon how well they cope. As Carol Burnett said, "Comedy is tragedy plus time."

Norman Cousins, the late editor of *The Saturday Review*, wrote *Anatomy of an Illness* and described how he used humor to overcome an incapacitating degenerative disease. His physicians had diagnosed him with an untreatable condition and told him that he faced years of increasing pain until his death. Cousins flatly refused to accept this prognosis. Instead, being a typically difficult-to-manage patient, he angered his doctors by checking out of the hospital and into a nearby hotel. There, he did two things. He undertook a regular program of exercise and good nutrition, and he spent a lot of time watching comic movies. He soon found that after a good dose of humor, he was able to sleep and rest without pain. Cousins then became adamant about being surrounded by hilarity in the form of old movies and records. Within months, the symptoms were in remission. It was the use of humor which he most greatly credited with his recovery.

Why is laughter such good medicine? Some research indicates that there is an increased level of a particular antibody secreted in the saliva following episodes of laughter. It's also been correlated with elevated levels of beta-endorphin in the bloodstream. Both the antibody and the beta-endorphin are released during periods of exercise, which hearty laughter actually is since it moves the entire chest and abdominal area.

There's also the fact that the focus of the humor creates a diversion, thereby masking opposing, more painful emotions, such as sadness or anger. When you laugh, it creates a condition of emotional interference by overriding the brain's ability to produce an opposing emotion, such as sadness.

Since we seldom laugh without stimulation from others, there is an element of socialization involved, as well, even if the person who's making us laugh is Allan King's voice on the radio or Groucho Marx's face on the movie screen. It doesn't matter that neither is alive because their wit and slapstick antics still are.

Realize that from birth your body has learned to associate smiling with warmth and security. From the moment you smiled at your mother, and she smiled back, the configuration of the facial muscles has taught your brain that you are experiencing a state of positive feelings. In the same way that the sound of the bell caused Pavlov's dogs to salivate, it may be that smiling triggers the emotion of pleasure.

Gallows humor is something we all experience at one time or another, and it often frightens us. No matter how inappropriate you may believe it is to laugh in the midst of tragedy, nor how rationally insensitive it may seem, release through the occasional sick joke is actually a coping skill, enabling you to balance the horror of the situation while keeping your emotions under control.

Try this to experience how effective it is. Force yourself to laugh. It needn't be laughter caused by actual mirth. Just smile and begin to emit the sound of laughter. If you're in a crowded room, all the better - you'll be able to laugh at how silly it is to laugh at nothing at all while those around you wonder what's wrong with you. If you laugh long enough in this situation, the others will join you, proving that laughter, like yawning, is contagious.

Pay attention to how you feel both during and after the laughter. Notice the way you breathe. Most people inhale deeply and exhale in short bursts. This is the exact opposite of the very shallow, rapid breathing pattern which occurs during periods of anxiety.

Try this in real life situations when fear, anxiety, sadness, or any other negative emotion interferes with your ability to enjoy good mental and physical health. Move your facial muscles into the form of a smile. The pleasure sensation the brain associates with smiling serves to neutralize the negative emotion being experienced.

- ❏ Humor as a coping tool allows you to maintain distance from and control over stressors.
- ❏ The physical activity involved with laughter creates positive chemical changes within your body.
- ❏ Laughter alters your breathing pattern and increases the amount of oxygen in your bloodstream.
- ❏ The act of smiling can both mask and circumvent negative emotions.
- ❏ Make a deliberate effort to laugh during stressful times. Every laugh is a powerful wave of recovery.

- The most important dimension of laughter is your ability to laugh at yourself during tough times. The message you send is, "Don't take yourself too seriously."
- Avoid making fun of others or using humor to throw a punch.
- A good 10 minute laugh session is powerful medicine. Build a laugh-tape library and make regular use of it. Remember, a sense of humor is learned. But so is the ability not to laugh; that also is learned.
- Make an effort to laugh or, at least, smile 50 or more times a day - most importantly, when you feel stress getting to you. Humor is serious business.

Gotta Get Rhythm When You've Got The Blues: Many people have the mistaken impression that good health can be achieved only through hard work and a certain amount of discomfort. Bland foods and countless hours in the gymnasium often are perceived as the price to pay for optimal health. This isn't true. There are many activities you can engage in that are highly pleasurable and conducive to a state of optimal health. One is music.

Think of music as a form of internal massage. Researchers have clearly shown that music moves physiology. Changes in heart rate, blood pressure, respiration rate, body temperature, endorphin release, and the levels of stress hormones have been documented. Music has been shown to have therapeutic value in emotional healing, in improving muscle coordination in patients with Parkinson 's disease, in stabilizing stroke patients suffering from neurological disease affecting speech, in pain management, and even in strengthening the immune system. Used properly, music can become a powerful force in recovery and healing. Some of the most beneficial effects of music appear to be mediated through increased endorphin and serotonin production.

Healing with music is evident throughout our history, from ancient Yogis to American Indians to primitive African tribes. The music of India, for example, which is called Ragas, is played at certain times of the day to tune up and balance the body. In the 6th century B.C., Pythagoras used music to facilitate harmony and health to the whole body. He prescribed a regimen to wake up by, to work by, and to relax and sleep by. From the Renaissance period to the present day, documented evidence exists showing that music and singing were used to lift spirits and to enhance the flow of positive emotions. Researchers today also have linked certain forms of music with relieving boredom and mental and physical fatigue.

The emotion-arousing ability of music has intrigued researchers. Happiness appears to follow fast tempos, simple harmonies, and flowing rhythms. Melody apparently plays a very small role in arousing particular emotions. Music written in the major chords is associated with happiness, gracefulness, playfulness, and merriment. The minor chords are usually sad and sentimental. Complex, dissonant harmonies can stimulate vigor and excitement. Classical music tends to gain more pleasant emotional value with repetition than popular music. Popular works reach a rapid peak in affective value, followed by a rapid decline in pleasantness with continued repetition.

Music is capable of both inflaming as well as taming the passions. By penetrating your very core, it can cause you to experience intense pleasure or to weep. Through its ability to modulate the expression of emotions, music has its greatest impact upon your health. Most music theories are predicated upon the association between music and emotions. More than 100 years ago, Herbert Spencer observed that when speech became emotional, the corresponding sound spanned a far greater tonal range and more approximated music than syntactical language. He believed that these fluctuations of sound eventually became separated from language and then evolved into a form of music. This is quite opposite to the viewpoint of Charles Darwin, who believed that music evolved as a form of sexual invitation, a tool with which to attract the attention of a potential mate. This conclusion was based upon observations of birdsong as well as evidence that the males of many species use their vocalization capabilities far more when under the influence of sexual feelings. I suppose it could be argued that the custom of women throwing panties onto the stage when being crooned by a popular performer might be a human version of this biologically-based behavior.

A more pragmatic viewpoint is that music evolved as a means by which to communicate information. For example, the singing voice has been found to carry over a greater distance than does the spoken voice. In fact, many wind instruments probably were invented for this purpose. Related to this interpretation is the observation that, in certain aboriginal cultures, songs were used to map the borders of territories. In essence, the contours of the territory were reflected directly in the contours of the melody.

Regardless of the precise origins of music, there is absolutely no question that it is a facilitator of social interaction. The behavior of dancing as well as hand clapping is an obvious manifestation of this. Music is used in religious ceremonies as well as in rites of passage in order to prepare people for action. It is used not only to facilitate the display of a particular emotion, but also to enhance the probability that all of those in the social group will be experiencing the same emotion at approximately the same time. Music does not necessarily cause an emotion. Instead, it has the ability to intensify or to highlight the emotion which might be elicited by some other event.

Extreme forms of arousal often are perceived as being painful or unpleasant. But, we all crave to have some milder form of excitement in our lives, which is actually life-enhancing. The physiological correlates of arousal are very similar, regardless of the particular emotion that is being elicited. For example, the original Kinsey report reveals that aggressive arousal and sexual arousal share in common 14 physiological changes. These include increased heart rate, muscle tone, and blood pressure. Of course, not all music is intended to induce arousal. Some forms do just the opposite. Either way, music is a powerful tool that can be used to enhance the emotional state that you wish to experience.

Music has many benefits in the context of health. It has very strong mnemonic properties. Many of us are able to recall the words of songs with much greater accuracy than we are able to recall prose. This also has been demonstrated in mentally retarded children, who have been found to be capable of recalling more material after it is presented to them in the form of song than when it is read to them simply as a story. Oliver Sacks, in his book *Awakenings*, described a patient who exhibited excitability as well as uncontrollable movements. Sacks goes on to describe how, "By far the best treatment of her crises was music, the effects of which were almost uncanny." In his other book, *The Man Who Mistook His Wife for a Hat*, Sacks describes a musician who, because of a neurological condition, was unable to recognize a number of common objects, although his musical abilities were largely unimpaired. Functioning was very difficult for this individual, unless he took care of his basic needs while singing. Indeed, music was the only means by which he was able to find structure in his environment. Music also has been found to enable people who stutter to communicate more readily. Mel Tillis, the popular Country and Western performer, has a difficult time communicating in spoken language, but he has no difficulty entertaining huge audiences through song. There is good reason for this. Language is dominant in the left hemisphere of the brain, while music awareness and expression is dominant in the right hemisphere. There is no reason why a pathological condition that impairs one activity should interfere with the other.

There are instances whereby music actually can impair health. Some individuals are susceptible to a condition called musicogenic epilepsy. As a result of the physical properties of music acting directly upon the brain, certain passages of especially arousing music have been shown to induce grand mal seizures. In some very rare instances, even the recollection of music can provoke these convulsions. Another detrimental side effect of music may well occur as a result of its widespread use in hospital operating theaters. Several years ago, a research paper published in one of the leading medical journals revealed that surgeons make fewer mistakes if they are able to listen to their favorite music while in the operating room. This is all well and good for the surgeon, but it may be detrimental to the patient in other ways. Implicit memory is sometimes thought of as the subconscious memory. There are certain types of anesthesia that actually preserve implicit memory, enabling you to recall events that might have occurred while you supposedly were deeply anesthetized. At least one case has been recorded in the legal journals in which a person recalled her surgeons making disparaging remarks about her obesity. Re-exposure to certain cues enabled her to recall those remarks, and she successfully sued her physicians. The same could happen with respect to any stimulus to which you might be exposed, including music. That previously therapeutic score may now elicit anxiety, having been associated with a hospital stay.

The Greeks of Plato's era believed that training in music was essential for full development. They recognized it as a powerful tool that could, indeed, alter the character of those who studied it. They also believed that certain types of music could be detrimental. A modern era application of the use of music for evil ends occurred during the days of Nazi Germany, when music was used to heighten the emotions of the crowds as well as a means by which to cloud their judgment. Not only did Hitler use music to manipulate the emotions of those who were listening to his speeches; he often used musical passages composed by Wagner to arouse himself. For Hitler, music was an energizing drug.

Music has been subject to censorship perhaps more than any other art form. During Stalin's Russia, American jazz was banned for many years because it was thought to be decadent. There is currently considerable debate as to whether or not certain forms of rap music should be censored because the messages conveyed are considered counter to the norms of society. Regardless of whether you agree or disagree with such censorship, these concerns do acknowledge the ability of music profoundly to influence the lives of those who listen to it.

If you are experiencing an excessive amount of anger or fear, then use music to facilitate the appearance of the emotional state you would rather be in or need to be in to achieve a state of optimal health. Whether music really induces feelings or simply evokes images and memories of feelings is debatable. Some argue that listening to music is nothing more than an escape from reality, and this may be the case under some circumstances. However, there is also overwhelming evidence that the physical properties of the sound waves are able to penetrate the inner recesses of the brain to induce very real physiological and emotional consequences. Use it.

The following guidelines were created by the performance coach, Dr. Jim Loehr, during the course of working with elite athletes:

- Make two separate music CD's of 12 to 15 minutes each. CD 1 should be music that energizes you, lifts your spirits, and puts you into a state of High Positive Energy. This is the music that pumps you up and stimulates feelings of confidence and empowerment. This is your positive fight--your warrior music. CD 2 should be music that relaxes you, slows you down, and enhances feelings of inner peace and harmony. This is your recovery--healing music.

- Sound tracks from movies and music without lyrics work best for most people. The idea is to move physiology in targeted directions with the help of music. Select what works best for you.

- Use your CD's daily to either facilitate positive energy and arousal or relaxation and recovery.

- New CD's need to be made approximately once a month to keep the impact strong and powerful.

- Combining visualization and imagery with the music dramatizes the effects.

Every Breath You Take: A crisis has just arisen. Don't let your physiology overwhelm you. Take immediate control. One of the most effective interventions was suggested by Judge Ito when, during a particularly heated moment of the O.J. Simpson trial, he admonished Marcia Clark to "take three, deep breaths." It was excellent advice. Controlling your breathing is an indirect means by which to exert control over many physiological processes. Breathing influences your blood gasses, which, in turn, affect heart rate. Furthermore, you really are controlling the neurotransmitters in the brain, which regulate the muscles of the diaphragm. Those same neurotransmitters can impact your perception and judgment. These are just a few of the benefits of controlled breathing:

❑ Helps to trigger a relaxation response
❑ Enables you to better focus
❑ Establishes an optimal level of oxygen in the body
❑ Induces a feeling of being in control
❑ May cool the brain

Breathing exercises also counteract the detrimental effects of rapid, shallow breaths. If it leads to hyperventilation, this can result in vascular changes in the brain, along with feelings of dizziness.

There are certain components of emotional responses that lie outside your control. The autonomic nervous system and neuroendocrine pathways are extremely difficult, if not impossible, for the average person to exert control over. Some highly skilled practitioners of yoga have been shown to have such mastery, but it requires years of intensive practice to achieve. Still, there are particular things which can be done that are subject to your conscious control and which, in turn, transmit signals to those systems within your body over which you have minimal influence.

You cannot consciously control the proportions of oxygen and carbon dioxide in your blood, but you can regulate your breathing and, in doing so, can transmit signals throughout the body which have the ultimate effect of stabilizing various physiological systems. If you experience the very rapid and shallow breathing often associated with fear and anxiety, this can create build-up of carbon dioxide in the bloodstream. Elevated CO_2 has been correlated with attacks of anxiety. Thus, while the anxious state occurred in response to something threatening in the environment, the emotional state is continued by the physiological consequences.

Simply drawing three, long, deep breaths - inhaling through the nose, filling the lungs, distending the diaphragm, and then exhaling slowly through the mouth - has a substantial effect on altering the chemical makeup of the blood and, therefore, on alleviating fear or anxiety. You'll not only find yourself energized; you indirectly will be controlling your physiology. This type of deep breathing normally is associated with the relaxation response, not with anxiety. Signals are transmitted into the nervous system, conveying to the body that it is actually in a relaxed state.

By inhaling through the nostrils, another effect occurs - the brain experiences a very slight drop in temperature. An elevation in brain temperature is associated with negative feelings, which explains why so many clichés have grown up around the concept, such as calling someone 'hot-headed,' or suggesting they 'chill out.'

There is still another benefit to engaging in deep breathing exercises; you almost immediately will feel different because you are actively doing something. And remember, it's not the stressor, but your feeling of helplessness, that is detrimental to your health. Breathing helps you take control.

❑ Deep breathing helps you distance yourself from the immediate stressor through an act you control.
❑ The body associates deep breathing with a state of relaxation, which leads to an enhanced emotional state.
❑ Deep breathing actually cools the brain and stabilizes the physiology.

Abdominal Breathing

• Lie down on a comfortable surface and place a light object on your stomach. A book or small pillow will be fine. While breathing, you want your abdomen to expand in response to downward movement of the diaphragm. This is the muscle that separates the abdominal cavity from the lungs. As the diaphragm moves down, air is drawn into the lower part of the lung. At the same time, your stomach will rise. By placing an object on your stomach, you will see this happen. Inhale slowly, hold the breath for a short interval, and then slowly exhale.

• Begin by doing a set of 10 deep breathing exercises. Then, as you become more adept, do three or more such sets. Be careful that you do not become lightheaded. This can happen when you start doing this for the first time. When you reach the point where you can breathe smoothly and rhythmically for five minutes, you will have mastered a time-honored technique for reducing stress. By the way, the reason for lying down is so that you can observe your abdomen rising as a confirmation that you are doing it correctly. After you know what to do, you can practice this technique in just about any comfortable setting - standing, sitting, or lying down.

Are you really in a bind? Is the pressure overwhelming? Then try this 15 second variation for an almost instant calming effect. Inhale slowly over a period of five seconds. Remember to use the diaphragm. Then, hold your breath for another five seconds before exhaling for another five. Take two regular breaths, and repeat the cycle. Keep doing this until you begin to feel calm.

The Benefits Of Relaxation: Relaxation counters stress and so, by extension, helps to undo the damage that stress does to the body. In addition, relaxation very well may have beneficial effects independent of its ability to counteract stress. That is, you will benefit from a relaxation protocol, regardless of whether you are experiencing stress. For example, many people have reported that a regular program of relaxation helps them to:

❑ Increase their energy level
❑ Enhance memory
❑ Lower blood pressure
❑ Enhance awareness of their emotional state
❑ Increase the restful stage of sleep
❑ Increase sense of control

Relaxation can be achieved in a number of different ways. Furthermore, it does not have to begin with a state of quiescence. A very effective way to achieve relaxation is to briefly exercise and, then, to allow heart rate, respiration rate, and the other physiological changes follow a natural, downward spiral. You will experience relaxation even though you may be out of breath. Indeed, many athletes report that exercise induces a state of relaxation when it's over. Whether this is due to the release of endorphins, which commonly occurs at the conclusion of exercise, or whether it is due to the altered kinetics is debatable. What's important is the fact that it works.

Regardless of which method you choose, each will be enhanced if you limit sensory distractions. Dim the light, select a room temperature that is neither too warm nor too cold, and wear loose, comfortable clothing. You want to reduce anything that might prove to be a distraction.

Touch Me In The Morning: Most mammalian species employ touch in the context of healing. Humans rub sore and tender spots, while animals lick the abrasion. A symbolic form of this behavior is a mother kissing her child's wound in order to make it better. It makes sense that touch would play an important role in your well-being when you realize that the skin is one of the largest organ systems of the body, and that it is constantly at the interface of the environment in which you reside. It is well documented in the acupuncture literature that applying pressure to certain regions of the body can, indeed, have a profound impact upon distant sites. There may be additional benefits.

When an animal is licking a wound, not only does this serve to cleanse the area, but, in recent years, very powerful substances have been detected in saliva, which are capable of exerting anti-microbial effects. These include powerful antibiotics. There is even a chemical which interferes with the ability of HIV to attach to target cells. There are many components of the behavior of touching that impact upon your health and well-being, depending upon the precise manner in which the touch is being applied.

Massage may induce a state of relaxation, which serves to counter the adverse effects of generalized stress. Massage has been found to reduce anxiety and depression in those suffering from chronic fatigue syndrome, in adolescent mothers, and in those who are HIV positive. This may explain the correlation between massage and elevated Natural Killer Cell activity and T-cell levels in those diagnosed with HIV.

Some massage therapists assert that massage may stimulate the movement of immune system cells within lymphatic channels in the body. It is argued that by engaging in a form of deep massage, one would be able to stimulate the migration of lymphocytes. This is not an unreasonable claim. It is essential that lymphocytes constantly move around the body in order to seek out pathogens. They move through the circulatory system as well as within the lymphatic channels. The lymphatic channels can be looked upon as a series of garden hoses that link the lymph nodes and the spleen. Lymph nodes and the white pulp of the spleen are those large filters where pathogens accumulate and where they come into contact with disease-fighting lymphocytes. But the lymphatics, in contrast to the circulatory system, have no heart. There is no equivalent pump. What enables the cells to move, albeit very sluggishly, from one lymph node to another is the peristaltic movement of muscles surrounding the lymphatic channels. An argument is made that by recreating that peristaltic movement through massage, one can facilitate lymphocyte trafficking. Regardless of whether the effects are direct or indirect, massage certainly has been found to have positive effects in treating a variety of immunologic illnesses, such as asthma, chronic fatigue syndrome, pediatric dermatitis, and HIV.

No one would question the fact that massage provides a form of escape. You temporarily are removed from stressful circumstances and, if relaxing in this manner is conducive to your personality, then it's clearly going to have beneficial effects. Furthermore, you might manifest stress in the form of muscle tension, which can be directly alleviated through massage. There also is a degree of social interaction which is very beneficial to your health.

Massage And Development Of Infants: There is no question that touch and massage not only are beneficial but absolutely essential in the context of early development. Tiffany Fields, a clinical psychologist, conducted a study in which premature infants were divided into one of two groups. One group was gently touched several times a day. Their backs and the backs of their legs were stroked. The other premature infants were handled only when it was necessary to change their diapers and when it was time for them to be fed. Otherwise, they were left alone. Those children who were touched grew at a rate that was over 30 percent greater than those children who were not touched. They attained their neurologic reflexes sooner and checked out of the hospital several days prior to the children who were not touched. At eight months of age, they even had motor and cognitive advantages over those children who were not touched.

Maggot Therapy: There's another form of massage which many people find rather disgusting, but which is returning as a treatment option. It is based upon an observation that was made during World War I. It was observed that those soldiers who were severely injured and who remained on the battlefield for several days before they could be tended to by health care workers often had speedier recoveries compared with those soldiers who were transported almost immediately to the first aid areas. In other words, those soldiers whose wounds became infested with flies and maggots actually were better off than those soldiers whose wounds were kept clean and had various medicines applied. It was the latter individuals whose limbs most often required amputation.

One interpretation is that the maggots were responsible for the observed healing. While seeking out infected and decaying tissue, the maggots also were gently massaging the healthy cells that were replacing those that were damaged. When their job was done, they sprouted wings and gently flew away. No need to rip away dressings containing growth and other healing substances. It also provided an opportunity for air to surround the injury which, in turn, promoted healing. As incredible as this may sound, maggot therapy is making a comeback. No, not in out of the way locations where people can't afford more modern techniques, but in major hospitals in large cities in the United States are maggots once again being utilized. This is because many of the antibiotics that were such powerful weapons a few decades ago now are practically useless in protecting us against the bacteria that they originally were designed to attack. This is due to the indiscriminate and inappropriate use of antibiotics in our society. Maggots, though, keep on working. In fact, deep bone infections seldom respond to antibiotics, but they always have responded reasonably well to maggot therapy.

One final interpretation of how massage might work is that it brings about harmony within energy meridians within the body. The role of energy meridians is the foundation for many forms of Oriental medicine, and this interpretation must not be excluded simply because it does not fit into the Western medical paradigm. I'm not suggesting that you embrace this interpretation with blind acceptance, but only that you keep an open mind about it.

Aromas And Aromatherapy: Some people claim that the sense of smell is a means by which to manipulate emotions. Proof of this claim is not available, although when considering how olfaction is mediated within the brain, it certainly is feasible. Most of the sensory systems course through the brain via a labyrinth of structures and pathways. For example, the sense of hearing as well as vision wends its way through the sensory apparatus, arriving initially within a structure called the thalamus. From this relay site, this information is transmitted to so-called 'higher brain centers,' where it is processed in ways that enable you to make the appropriate decision about what is happening in the environment. Eventually, all of the information arrives in the amygdala, which is the brain's emotional computer. The sense of smell is different. Olfactory information is able to short-circuit many of the higher brain areas and to plunge directly into the emotional brain. Some of the information goes into the part of the brain which controls the autonomic nervous system as well as many of the hormonal pathways which are activated during stress. This very well may explain the well-documented association between the sense of smell and those behaviors that are linked with emotions. They would include sex as well as aggression. Many species actually recognize each other, as well as their emotional state, on the basis of smell alone.

There's a very good reason why the sense of smell is processed differently, at least in mammals. Most mammals depend upon visual information to negotiate their environments. Furthermore, the type of information coming in through the visual system is relatively complete and enables us to respond almost immediately. For example, during the Stone Age, if a meat-eating dinosaur were to see a small object scurrying across a field, it would have been able to make the immediate decision that this was something to eat. On the other hand, if it saw a very large animal, indeed one larger than itself, it probably would have enough information to know that it should flee. However, if that same animal caught the odor of something, a large amount of cognition would be required in order to make the appropriate decision. If it were the scent of a female dinosaur that a male happened to identify, he would need to recall her normal repertoire of behaviors and tap into a variety of cognitive centers in order to determine where she most likely would be. So it was very important that the memory of past experience become very closely associated with the sense of smell.

This, along with other research, clearly reveals that there is a pathway by which olfactory information is able to enter those areas of the brain that are intimately involved with the expression of emotions. That does not necessarily mean that these pathways still are being used. They could be left over from some period in our evolution which has no functional purpose at all in modern society. Let's briefly review the evidence that, in certain contexts, proves that odors can have a profound impact both upon our physiology as well as upon our behavior.

The Scent Of A Woman: It is the study of reproductive pheromones which provides the most convincing argument that aromas can impact upon your health. Pheromones are molecules emitted into the environment by a number of species. They communicate information from one member of that specie to another. Fish, rats, dogs, and even humans rely upon them. Some evoke the emotion of fear, others anger, but those that have been most extensively studied are those that elicit the emotions associated with arousal of the reproductive system.

The most convincing documentation that pheromones do function in human society is to be found in those situations where women live together. Women who live in college dormitories with many other women have been found to have synchronized menstrual cycles. The same is true of women who live on the same floor in prisons. In addition, men and women each produce chemicals which serve as an attractant for the member of the opposite gender. Short chain fatty acids called *copulins* have been identified in the vaginal secretions of a variety of female primates, with the amount of copulin increasing as estrogen rises. When men are exposed to a large number of odors, they will exhibit preference for secretions containing copulin. In addition to men being attracted to copulin, which is found at highest concentrations at the time of ovulation, women are attracted to a chemical called *exaltalide*. It is a macrocyclic ketone which children, men, and post-menopausal women have a very difficult time detecting, unless they are given estrogen. Studies have revealed that not only will exposure to exaltalide affect the judgment of women when evaluating the written and interviewed descriptions of male job candidates, but they selectively will seek out and sit on chairs which contain a trace amount of this chemical.

This is the basis of the perfume industry. People wear fragrances primarily for the purpose of making themselves attractive to members of the opposite sex. If you question this conclusion, try to recall if you have ever seen an advertisement for a fragrance which would make the wearer smell like an engineer, a school teacher, or a nurse. Of course not. That's not why they are marketed. Not only are they marketed as sexual attractants, but it is the perfume industry that has sponsored much of the research delving into the nature of reproductive pheromones. It is noteworthy that women are 10,000 times more sensitive to aromas at the time of ovulation as compared with other intervals during the menstrual cycle. This, undoubtedly, enables them to identify a male when the probability of procreation is optimal. Of course it works in the other direction as well since men are attracted to copulin, which is produced most when women are ovulating. This may explain why oral sex has such an intimate impact. The exchange of bodily odors is forced to occur and, undoubtedly, serves as a means of social communication.

Aromatherapy: The observations made in the context of reproductive pheromone research clearly reveal that trace amounts of chemicals can make their way into key areas of our brains and arouse not only the endocrine physiology that is paramount for reproduction to occur, but also libido and other behavioral manifestations of procreation. Is it really that far fetched to propose that other types of odors might also arouse other physiological systems, including those that affect your health? This is the basis of aromatherapy. It is predicated upon the belief that essential oils found in plants are capable of imparting fragrances that are capable of affecting not only emotions but also mental and physical well-being. For example, the fragrance associated with lavender is believed to

79

be relaxing and serves as a gentle sedative. Rosemary, on the other hand, is thought to have the opposite effect and serves to stimulate. And rose oil is said to be able to calm the emotions of anger. Claims are made about many other fragrances, as well.

There are three forms of aromatherapy. *Holistic aromatherapy* is the first and incorporates the use of essential oils, often in the context of massage. The second form is *medical aromatherapy,* in which specific fragrances are prescribed in order to counter various maladies. Finally, *aesthetic aromatherapy* involves the use of oils and fragrances to treat skin problems, such as stretch marks. It's also used to induce a state of relaxation. While the use of aromatherapy dates back 5,000 years to the days of the early Egyptians, the form of aromatherapy practiced in Western society dates to 16th century Germany. A large number of claims are made regarding the use of aromatherapy. Conditions ranging from arthritis and allergies, to anger and depression are thought to be affected by different aromas. Whether these claimed benefits really are due to something associated with the chemical configuration of the odor-inducing molecule or simply the evocation of memory is hard to discern. Many people do associate fragrances with certain situations or people, and it may be the memory of that circumstance which is actually evoking the emotional state. Of course, the same odor may evoke completely different states, depending upon the nature of one's memory. When evaluating such claims against the backdrop of data collected under well-controlled circumstances in the arena of reproductive pheromones, I believe they should be given serious consideration.

At least one study conducted in mice under well-controlled laboratory conditions has revealed that, when animals are exposed to a stressor, they produce a type of pheromone that is capable of inhibiting the immune system of other mice. This included a reduction in the proliferation of antibody-producing cells as well as the proliferation of T-cells, which coordinate so many aspects of the immune system. It was concluded that the mechanism, most likely, was activation of the brain circuitry that gives rise to elevated stress chemicals. These are the same chemicals that are capable, at high concentrations, of suppressing the immune system.

Environmentalize Your Surroundings: Let's consider a very practical way in which you can utilize this information in dealing with emotions. You might start by environmentalizing your surroundings. If you had a bad experience in your office, re-exposure to some fragrances might evoke the same physiological and psychological consequences that you experienced at the time the event happened. In other words, conditioning may be occurring. If you can, reduce your exposure to those odors. On the other hand, certain fragrances may elicit memories of very pleasant emotional states. If that is the case, then seek out those fragrances in order to induce the state you wish to evoke. And who knows? Perhaps some of the claims made by aromatherapists are valid. It's unlikely that a therapy would have endured for thousands of years if there weren't some basis for it. Use your body as a laboratory, and discover which fragrances work for you in helping you to win the stress challenge.

- By circumventing pathways employed by the other senses, the sense of smell allows you to experience more rapid emotional reactions to events.

- Possibly because of past memories associated with certain scents, aromas can be used to induce positive emotional states.

It Hurts So Bad: Pain profoundly interferes with the ability to enjoy emotional or physical pleasure in life. Just as perceived control enables you better to cope with stress, control also enables you to endure greater amounts of pain.

When it was first suggested that terminal cancer patients be allowed to control the amount of pain medication they received, physicians were gravely concerned about the potential for over-medication, as this might lead to addiction or, even worse, death. Yet exactly the opposite proved to be true. Patients given control over their pain medications actually used fewer and lower dosages and reported less pain than patients who received medications on a schedule set by the health provider.

Pain is one of the less-than-pleasant facts of life which we must all cope with at varying times in varying degrees. Here are a few suggestions for dealing with it:

❑ **Accept the pain rather than becoming locked into an emotional battle with it.** Accepting the pain as part (but not all) of your experience can reduce its grip on your ability to function. Pain exists to make you aware of a part of you that needs care. Consider it a by-product of a healing process going on within your body. Work with this function rather than against it, and healing will be facilitated.

❑ **Create a diversion for yourself.** Use imagery to mentally transport yourself to a setting that is pleasant and painless. Note any physical and emotional circumstances that make the pain worse, and take steps to avoid those circumstances.

❑ **Try to relax.** Seek out a tranquil setting, get comfortable, breathe, and meditate. Just focusing on your breath as you inhale and exhale can provide an effective diversion.

❑ **Change your diet.** If pain is triggered by inflammation, realize that saturated fats, especially those found in meats and dairy products, can aggravate inflammatory pain. So can caffeine, which tends to increase tension. On the other hand, nutrients such as calcium and magnesium help relax muscles. Some evidence also suggests that a diet rich in carotenes and vitamins E and C can help decrease sensitivity to the pain of inflammation.

❑ **Pursue some social support for yourself.** Having others around can serve as a distraction from pain. Being lonely can trigger depression or make discomfort feel worse.

❑ **Take control of your situation.** A person who has control over events is able to endure more adversity than a person who has no control at all.

Most stress-related chemical changes are highly adaptive. They have evolved for the purpose of getting us out of short-term emergency situations. Problems arise when they persist for months or even years. For example, blood pressure will rise as a result of a stress-induced increase in heart rate. Furthermore, as a result of the metabolic changes that occur within your body, there can be a build-up of cholesterol, resulting in a reduction in the diameter of the blood vessel lumen. If blood pressure remains elevated for an extended period of time, damage to the inside lining of the blood vessels can occur and, especially in post-menopausal women, result in hypertensive stroke.

There are behavioral interventions that may help. George Engel, a famous psychologist, conducted an experiment in which he trained monkeys to either increase or decrease their heart rate in order to avoid a mild stressor. This and other types of studies provide the most convincing evidence that biofeedback works. Put on a heart rate monitor and try this simple exercise:

A Simple Biofeedback Exercise

1. Find a comfortable place to sit.
2. Measure your heart rate.
3. Inhale and exhale, all the while observing how your heart rate responds.
4. Concentrate on lowering your heart rate. Adjust the tempo of your breathing until the beats per minute start to decline.

Now try to increase your heart rate without resorting to physical   activity.

LEARNING STRESS - RECOVERY

Most people know how to experience stress. That's not the problem. The problem is that very few of us know adequately how to respond to stress. As odd as it may sound, it actually is possible to train your body to withstand stress.

Every cell within the cardiovascular system, the respiratory system, and even the immune system has the ability to learn to withstand stress. It is well-documented that if the concentration of a chemical increases within the body, there will be a corresponding adjustment in the ability of the receptor to attract the chemical. It's one of the ways the body adapts to change. By bathing the body's cells in stress hormones during their episodic release, the cells learn to recover; and, then, when a major stressor arises, these cells are better able to adapt.

The best form of stress from which to train recovery is exercise, yet very few people take advantage of this powerful tool. Some studies suggest that the average person spends two and a half hours a day watching television, yet only 15 minutes per day exercising. Many people get no exercise at all. Never in the course of history have people been more inactive, and never have we been more susceptible to so many diseases. Physical activity of any kind will help protect you against coronary arterial disease, colon cancer, breast cancer, and, without question, obesity and all of its health consequences.

Cross-Stressing Through Exercise: There is a medical syndrome sweeping the United States. It is characterized by being out of breath, post-exertional exhaustion, chronic muscle tension, obesity, high blood pressure, fatigue, and difficulty falling asleep and awakening refreshed. No, it's not Chronic Fatigue Syndrome. I call it Chronic Sedentary Syndrome, and there's not a thing your doctor can do. The treatment is in your own hands, and it is 100 percent effective. The elixir is called EXERCISE!

"Before engaging in a new or different exercise program, first see your doctor."

Everyone who has opened an exercise book or door to a gym has been greeted with this ominous warning. While it is advisable, it simultaneously conveys a subtle and potentially dangerous message: exercise is dangerous.

Yes, it is true that high impact activities or misuse of some forms of equipment can be detrimental to your health. Exercise-induced joint injury, asthma, and cardiovascular ailments come to mind, along with other examples. Some forms of exercise can be dangerous, but not nearly as dangerous as the failure to exercise. Sedentary behavior stands shoulder to shoulder with smoking and high levels of cholesterol as a risk factor for coronary arterial disease. Our bodies are designed for movement, and, without it, dire consequences can occur. Therefore, my recommendation is:

"If you do not exercise, please see your doctor."

Exercise is a form of stress. No, it's not in the same category as losing a job or a loved one because, in terms of exercise, you are in control. Nonetheless, exercise and stress do have some shared features, enough of them that you can actually use exercise as a means by which to train yourself to better cope with stress. They are:

- Increased heart rate
- Increased respiration rate
- A switch from anabolism to catabolism
- Decreased salivation
- Inhibition of digestion

How does this stress training program work? While each stressful experience and your response are unique, there are some features that occur in everyone. Thus, when your body learns to adapt to one form of stress, you are able to better cope with most other forms. It's like learning to drive a car. No two automobiles are exactly the same; yet, having learned to drive one model, you readily can apply your basic driving skills to all others. You may have to search for the light switch or the hood release button, but the essential components are about where you would expect them. The same applies to stress. It's called *cross-stressing*. Once you learn to respond to one form of stress, you will have the basic skills to respond to most all other types. Exercise is the form of stress that you are going to use for training.

Calculate Your Maximum Heart Rate: Begin by calculating your maximum heart rate, which is the number of beats per minute (BPM) that cannot be exceeded when you increase the intensity of your exercise. In other words, if your heart were a car, it would be the highest number on your speedometer. The engine might be capable of going faster, but the needle on the gauge won't go any higher. There are several ways that you can determine your maximum BPM. I recommend that you take a stress test. Under a doctor's supervision, you exercise to the point where your heart rate levels off. Even though you run faster, your heart rate pegs out. This method will enable you to identify your precise maximum under medical supervision.

Some very fit individuals will test themselves using a heart rate monitor. Be careful. You will be pushing your heart to its maximum, which may unmask a latent heart condition. For this reason, I don't recommend this approach. A less accurate but better alternative to pushing yourself to the limit uses a simple mathematical formula. Subtract your age from 220 if you are a man, or 226 if you are a woman. Sample calculations for a 40 year old man and woman are as follows:

WOMAN (age 40)	MAN (age 40)
226 − 40 = 186 bpm	220 − 40 = 180 bpm

Why the difference? A woman's heart tends to be smaller than a man's. Consequently, a woman's heart has to beat at a slightly faster rate to maintain a comparable blood volume. As noted previously, this very simple calculation is not very accurate. It assumes that all men and women of the same age are basically the same, and it fails to take into account medical problems, genetics, or the type of exercise being performed. A person who is very fit may have a measured maximum heart rate 10 to 20 beats per minute faster than the value calculated using the formula. Furthermore, many athletes discover that their maximum heart rate for bicycling is quite different than that for running. Swimming may yield yet another value. Despite its flaws, you, at least, will have a starting point.

Determine Your Stress Zones: Next, calculate your high, medium, and low stress zones. These are based upon some of the same guidelines that athletes use to determine their aerobic and anaerobic zones. *Aerobic* means oxygen is being used. *Anaerobic* is without oxygen. If you exercise at an intensity that leaves you short of breath, chances are your body will not have enough oxygen to maintain aerobic-based pathways to generate energy. That's when you shift to anaerobic pathways to produce the energy you need to keep pace with the physical demands that you are placing on your body. This is very important if your objective is to lose weight. That's because plenty of oxygen is needed for fat to be converted into energy. If your workout is too intense, fat will be spared while you derive energy from stored glycogen – a process that does not require oxygen.

Low Stress Zone is where you should start if you have not exercised before, or if you are recovering from an injury. When you are in this zone, your heart rate will be between 50 and 60 percent of your maximum. Complete the calculation to determine your low stress zone.

Low Stress Zone

Max HR _____ x 0.60 = _____ bpm

Max HR _____ x 0.70 = _____ bpm

Moderate Stress Zone activity will help you increase your endurance for the stress of exercise. Your heart will beat at a faster rate because it will be bathed in larger amounts of adrenaline and other stress-related chemicals that speed your heart. The number of beats per minute will be between 60 and 70 percent of your maximum. At the same time, your body will become accustomed to this change so that when similar events occur under circumstances outside of your control, your body will be able to recover more efficiently. You will be breathing rapidly, but you'll still be able to obtain enough oxygen to maintain aerobic metabolism.

Moderate Stress Zone

Max HR _____ x 0.70 = _____ bpm

Max HR _____ x 0.80 = _____ bpm

High Stress Zone is the zone within which your body will learn to recover from an even greater amount of stress. When in this zone, your heart rate will be between 80 and 90 percent of your maximum, and the average person will not be able to take in enough oxygen to sustain some of the more common processes for obtaining energy. Your body will switch to anaerobic metabolism. Calculate the limits of this zone. Once you have all the numbers, you can create your own customized cross-stressing program.

High Stress Zone

Max HR _____ x 0.80 = _____ bpm

Max HR _____ x 0.90 = _____ bpm

You now have all the information needed to train yourself to better recover from stress. And that is the key--learning to recover. It's important to realize that stress causes harm when the intensity of the stressor overwhelms your capacity to cope. In other words, you feel helpless. Exercise is a form of stress, but it is one over which you have total control. You determine the start time, the intensity, as well as when to end the regimen. Consequently, you are subjecting your body to many of the same physiological events that occur during uncontrollable stress, but without the harmful consequences. That's why exercise is going to be used to induce a form of stress so that you can practice recovery.

Set Your Limits: Identify your personal stress zones using the formulas discussed above. The table below summarizes the heart rate that corresponds to the different zones.

Low Stress	60 to 70 % of maximum heart rate
Moderate Stress	70 to 80 % of maximum heart rate
High Stress	80 to 90 % of maximum heart rate

A Stress-Recovery Workout: There are many ways that people exercise. One is called *steady-state aerobics.* Typically, a person will exercise for a set period of time at the same intensity. They might run 5 miles or work out on a bicycle for 30 minutes. That certainly is a wonderful form of exercise, especially from the standpoint of building endurance or burning off fat. The following depicts the heart rate of a person engaged in *steady-state aerobics.*

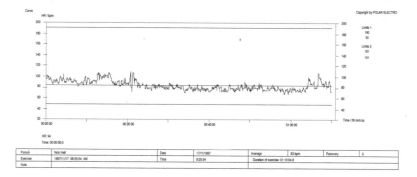

If you look closely, you'll notice that there is no opportunity for recovery until the end of the regimen, and then only a single period of recovery. In other words, this person is getting a good work-out, but he is not providing the body with an

91

opportunity to recover. Compare the steady-state workout with the following cross-stressing regimen.

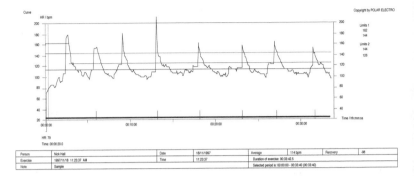

Notice how the heart rate is pushed to the upper levels of the high stress zone and then is allowed to recover. This person is exercising in a manner that incorporates no less than 8 recovery cycles into the program. Each time heart rate is elevated, the body is learning to adjust to greater amounts of stress. Each episode of stress is then followed by a period of recovery. Why is this beneficial for your health? It's beneficial because many of the same chemical events that occur during the *stress* of exercise occur during stressors over which you may have little control. There's little difference between a rise in heart rate when you are cut off by an eighteen-wheeler, and the increase that occurs when you voluntarily put demands on your body for more oxygen. However, since exercise is taking place on your terms, it's comparatively harmless.

Plan on spending approximately 80 percent of your workout within the moderate stress zone. This corresponds to the aerobic zone and will improve your cardiovascular fitness. The remaining time should be spent oscillating between the low and high stress zones as you create a wave-like pattern of heart rate change. When your heart rate reaches 90 percent of your maximum, slow down until it gradually descends to 60 percent. Then repeat the cycle, perhaps reaching 85 percent. Allow your heart rate to drop to about 65 percent. In doing this, you are incorporating a universal principle into your workout:

"For every action, there should be an equal and opposite reaction."

Or, for every episode of stress (increased heart rate), there needs to occur an equal amount of recovery (a decline in heart rate).

Choosing A Form Of Exercise: It really doesn't matter what form of exercise you choose. What is important is that you do something you enjoy. However, it is important to recognize that some exercise regimens enable you to attain a higher heart rate than others do.

The following table lists common aerobic activities, comparing them to running, which is the most common. Therefore, running is arbitrarily assigned a factor of 1. Lower numbers mean it is easier to attain a higher heart rate, while a higher number means more effort will need to be expended. For example, compared with running, a bicyclist would have to work between 10 and 20 percent harder in order to achieve the same heart rate. This is because cycling is a non-weight bearing exercise.

Running	1.0
Aerobics	0.9-1.1
Cycling	1.1-1.2
Mountain Biking	1.0-1.1
Stepping	1.0-1.2
Canoeing	1.2-1.3
Rowing	0.9-1.2
Walking	1.1
Swimming	1.2-1.3

Tennis	1.0
Badminton	1.1-1.2
Squash	1.0-1.1
Soccer	1.0
Skating	1.1-1.2
Cross-country Skiing	0.9

(From *The Heart Rate Monitor Book,* Polar Electro, Inc.)

The Conversation Rule: Some people prefer a simpler approach to life. Heart rate monitors, formulas for calculating maximum heart rate, and worrying about the upper and lower limits of different zones of activity may be all the incentive you need to reject totally the recommendations to be found in this section. If this applies to you, then forget the monitors and calculations. Use the following rules to determine in which zone you are:

Low Stress	Converse with ease
Moderate Stress	Converse with difficulty
High Stress	Unable to converse

YOU ARE WHAT YOU EAT

What You Eat May Be What's Eating You: The foods you eat can influence the chemicals within the brain that are so important to achieving certain emotional states. Just as there are different types of fuels for machines, different foods can have a profound impact on the machine that is the human body. Athletes are highly aware of this and tend to be very finicky about what they put into their bodies prior to competition. They know that food can affect their performance, as well as their emotional well-being. Some people call this concept *psychodietetics*. The name doesn't really matter. What does is the fact that foods can and do have a profound effect on your mood.

It's ironic that nutrition is, without question, the most important component of your health, yet we know so little about it. We know what starving children in Third World countries need, and we know a great deal about what to feed our dogs, cats, birds, and fish. We also know what specific nutrients and vitamins can do to cells in tissue structure. Nevertheless, how much of what form of what food and when it should be consumed are questions that continue to perplex us.

Have you ever felt sluggish a couple of hours after lunch, finding it difficult to concentrate and even to keep your eyes open? This is a perfectly natural occurrence, especially in our culture, which revolves around three square meals a day. And it happens for a number of reasons. First is how rapidly the food is converted into blood sugar, which triggers insulin production. Insulin maintains blood sugar at a fairly constant level. If the blood sugar rises rapidly, the body may release a little too much insulin, causing an overcompensation, which then sends the blood sugar plummeting. It's all part of the natural fluctuation, and it is nature's way of ensuring a balance of energy in the body between meals.

Also prompting that mid-afternoon sluggishness is another natural occurrence: body temperature actually drops during this time of day, just enough to facilitate the induction of sleep. Unfortunately, our historically-based Puritan work ethic tells us that taking an afternoon nap is a sign of laziness. If the boss catches you catching 40 winks around 3 p.m., you'll likely be passed over for the next promotion, if not shown the door. However, if the boss were really smart, she'd be following the example of so many other countries, where the afternoon siesta is an accepted part of the day, and productivity doesn't suffer.

So what can you do to control these fluctuations in your body?

- Eat more often, but eat less. Instead of three large meals each day, consume the food over five or even eight smaller feedings. This will maintain your blood sugar at a more constant level.

- Stay away from candy. There's no question a candy bar provides energy - but only for a few minutes. All that refined sugar sends the blood sugar soaring; but, ultimately, it drops even lower than before the candy bar was eaten, and you feel even more lethargic.

- Snack on a piece of fruit or whole grain breads. Their complex carbohydrates allow the body to maintain a steadier blood sugar level.

- Choosing foods wisely can help you more easily accomplish your tasks and goals. If you're working on a project that requires sharp focus and mental alertness, eat a meal rich in proteins, which energize you. After a hectic day, eat a dinner high in carbohydrates, such as pasta, to help you unwind and get a good night's sleep.

Are you aware that chocolate is both a food and a drug? Along with a small amount of caffeine, chocolate contains another chemical with effects similar to caffeine. Research has linked chocolate to an increase in adrenaline level by almost 10-fold. As a consequence, chocolate has an impact upon both the body and the mind, and it can truly be addictive.

Interestingly, many *chocoholics* are women, many of whom crave chocolate most intensely just prior to the onset of menstruation. Because of the cyclical timing of the craving, some nutritionists believe chocolate may alleviate symptoms associated with premenstrual syndrome. Many women claim that chocolate acts as an antidepressant for them. Unfortunately, the large amount of sugar in chocolate may predispose some people, especially women, to yeast infections, as well as to arthritis and asthma. It also may be correlated with hyperactivity, irritability, aggression, and other assertive-type behaviors in children.

Cheeseburger In Paradise—Not! As a nation, we have become obsessed with fat, both the amount we carry on our bodies and the amount we consume. And well we should be concerned about that fat. Dietary fat has been linked with obesity, cancer, and heart disease. In 1980, one out of four people was obese. Now, it's one out of three and getting worse. The rates of breast, colon, and prostate cancers are on the rise, and heart disease is the No. 1 killer of both men and women. All of these diseases directly are linked to fat consumption. Despite the constant bombardment of information through the media, from health-care providers and even from food labels, Americans are heavier than ever before. Since people claim to be eating less fat, why does this paradox exist? It exists probably for a variety of reasons. The average person doesn't have a clue about what they actually are consuming because food labels are misleading. Fat content may be expressed as a total percentage of the food, as a percentage of the daily minimum requirement, or in grams, all of which require an educated, analytical ability held by few people, other than dietitians and nutritionists.

Frankly, the information we receive is terribly confusing. For example, not all fat is the same. Monounsaturated and polyunsaturated fats are less harmful to the arteries than highly saturated fats found in meat, dairy products, and coconut oil. So, to interpret the effect on the body of that fat noted on the food label, it's also important to be aware of what type of fat it actually is.

Compounding the issue is that, while polyunsaturated fats found in corn, sunflower, and other oils are less harmful than saturated fats, polyunsaturates are not nearly as effective in lowering the so-called *bad cholesterol* as are the monounsaturated fats in olive and canola oils. In fact, there is evidence that monounsaturated fats not only reduce the bad cholesterol, but that they also augment levels of the good cholesterol by helping transport artery-clogging factors from the bloodstream.

Even the term *fat-free* does not mean that. FDA regulations dictate that for a product to make such a claim, it only must contain less than one-half gram of fat per serving. *Reduced-fat* means the product contains 25% less fat than its regular version. The term *low-fat*, with the exception of milk, means that the product has no more than three grams of fat per serving.

Milk labeling really adds to the confusion. When you see *2% low-fat* % on the milk label, you're likely to assume that means it has a 2% fat content. No. Two percent milk derives about 36% of its calories from fat. That's better than the 50% of calories from fat in whole milk, but it is certainly a far cry from the perception inferred from the large print on the label. So be very wary of labeling claims, and be careful to read all the fine print.

As confusing as the fat issue is, the solution is simple. We should consume no more than 20% of our calories in fat, no matter what its source. Even the beef industry endorses no more than a three-and-a-half-ounce serving of meat per meal. How can you gauge the correct portion? It's just about the same size as a deck of cards. You won't often see that size serving on a plate in a fancy restaurant.

As important as it is to limit dietary intake of fats, some research indicates that by adulthood, it may be too late to alter any link to correlated cancers. Two variables have been correlated with breast cancer -- increased height and age of menstruation onset, both of which are determined, in part, by the intake of dietary fat. It's important to instill healthy nutritional habits early and to keep dietary fat intake at the recommended 20% level for children above the age of two. Extra fat is called for, though, during the initial phase of growth. The best way for parents to do this is by setting a good example through their own eating habits.

When it comes to adding vitamin and mineral supplements to the diet, do so wisely. It is far better to receive the proper nutrients through the foods which naturally deliver them. Research has yet to prove that supplements in capsule or pill form work in the same protective manner that natural sources provide. Most of these supplements, when present in larger amounts than are necessary, simply are flushed from the body by the kidneys. And some, like vitamin A, can build up to toxic levels.

As a society, Americans are known to have the most expensive urine in the world. In the United States, we spend an average of $13.30 per person on vitamins each year. The Germans spend $9.81; the French $7.40; in Britain, it's $6.01, and in

Spain, only 48¢. And there's no conclusive evidence that links the amount spent with the health of people.

❑ What you eat and when you eat can have a direct impact upon your emotional states.

❑ Eating habits developed as children may have greater impact on adult health and well-being than changing those dietary habits as adults.

❑ Nutrients provided through their natural food sources are more valuable to the body and mind than dietary supplements.

Getting Started: Let's keep the priorities straight. It's not the stressor about which you are concerned. Instead, your concern is the impact it will have on your body. Your response to the stressor will determine if your capacity for productivity, pleasure, or health will be affected. No two people will respond in the same manner to a stressor. However, your unique way of responding can be optimized provided you take certain steps. Create a nutritional stage upon which every reaction within your body will be able to function with maximum efficiency. These guidelines will be the same for everyone. And don't allow stress to interfere with this extremely important component of your health.

All the recommendations in this section are guidelines. Use them as a starting point, and then experiment. Vary both the amounts of food as well as their proportions while simultaneously monitoring your mental, physical, and emotional states. Begin with the USDA guidelines. Obviously, they will not work for everyone, but it's a well thought out starting point.

Milk products are important because they provide protein, vitamins, and minerals. Milk, yogurt, and cheese are the best sources of calcium. The

Food Guide Pyramid suggests 2 to 3 servings of milk, yogurt, and cheese a day – 2 for most people, and 3 for women who are pregnant or breast-feeding, teenagers, and young adults to age 24. Meat, poultry, and fish are important because they supply protein, B vitamins, iron, and zinc. The other foods in this group – dry beans, eggs, and nuts – are similar to meats in providing protein and most vitamins and minerals. The Food Guide Pyramid suggests 2 to 3 servings each day of foods from this group. The total amount of these servings should be the equivalent of 5 to 7 ounces of cooked lean meat, poultry, or fish per day. Fruits and fruit juices are important because they provide large amounts of vitamins A and C and potassium. They are low in fat and sodium. The Food Guide Pyramid suggests 2 to 4 servings of fruits a day. Vegetables are important because they provide vitamins (such as vitamins A and C and folate) and minerals (such as iron and magnesium). They are naturally low in fat and also provide fiber. The Food Guide Pyramid suggests 3 to 5 servings of these foods a day. Breads, cereals, rice, and pasta are important because they provide complex carbohydrates (starches), which are an important source of energy, especially in low-fat diets. They also provide vitamins, minerals, and fiber. The Food Guide Pyramid suggests 6 to 11 servings of these foods a day. The small tip of the Pyramid shows fats, oils, and sweets. These are foods such as salad dressings and oils, cream, butter, margarine, sugars, soft drinks, candies, and sweet desserts. These foods provide calories and little else nutritionally. Most people should use them sparingly. The tip of the pyramid consists of added fat and sugar that do not naturally occur in the food item. (From 1997 ESHA Research)

The total number of calories you need will vary depending upon how active you are. A very active, middle-aged male may well require in excess of 3,000 calories per day, while a comparatively inactive individual will be better off with less than 2,000 calories.

- **Slow down when eating.** As food fills your stomach, messages are transmitted to the brain signaling that you are full and don't need any more. However, this takes time. If you eat too quickly, you may eat more than you need because by the time the signals arrive in the brain, you already have started on seconds.

- **Separate needs from wants.** When you have eaten enough to want more, but you don't really need it, push your plate away. That point will vary, depending upon how active you are. Not only will you achieve balance between energy replenishment and expenditure, but research reveals that you probably will live longer as well.

How Many Calories Do I Need? How do you know how many calories you actually need? Here are three easy steps to help you approximate the number of calories you need.

1. Start by multiplying your body weight by 11. The number you write down will be the number of calories that you need in order to make sure that your body works. After all, you do need calories in order to operate the muscles of the heart and lungs, as well as to fuel all of the other vital activities that are going on within your body. This number is your required amount of base calories.

2. In step two, determine your activity level. You actually might need help with this, so ask a couple of your friends or family members to give their opinion, too, as this is rather subjective. Your perception of high activity may not agree with somebody else's, and the guidelines are really just average determinations. As you go from sedentary to strenuous, write down the following percents. If you are sedentary, your percent is 30 to 50. If your activities are light, 55 to 65. Moderate, 65 to 70, and strenuous, 75 to 100. Now multiply your base number of calories by the two percentages corresponding to your activity level. If you are a moderate exerciser, then you will multiply your minimal level of calories by 65 percent and also by 70

percent. The lower number will be the minimal number of extra calories that you will need, while the higher number represents the maximum number of extra calories needed.

Activity	Description	Percent
Sedentary	No planned activity	30 to 50
Light	Occasional slow walk/ stroll	55 to 65
Moderate	Brisk walking or bicycling	65 to 70
Strenuous	Out of breath exercise	75 to 100 .

3. The third step really is quite easy. Simply add the low and high percentage values to your minimal base calories, and this will give you the approximate range of calories that you need on a weekly basis. Keep track of the amount of fat, carbohydrate, and protein in the foods you eat. Remember, these are the percentages you should have in your diet on a weekly basis. That's right – weekly. You have to be realistic. When your boss is hosting a dinner, it would be rude to pull out a calorie guide. Furthermore, there are times when starvation may be the only alternative to fast food or pizza, so you occasionally will consume foods which, by all rights, should turn your cardiovascular system into a Jiffy Lube. However, every seven days, this is what you should be close to:

Carbohydrates	**55 %**
Protein	**25 %**
Fat	**20 %**

Healthy Choices: If you are not careful, you may well fall victim to an advertising blitz which has the fast food industry spending more than any other industry. They are offering larger portions along with added value packages. In other words, buy the deluxe burger, and they'll throw in the large fries and an extra large drink. Let's not even consider the add-ons. Hardee's Monster Burger, draped in cheese and bacon, will, by itself, provide you with 970 calories. Stop at Long John Silver's, and order the Blazin' Cajun Shrimp Wrap, and you'll walk out with 1,419 additional calories. You probably already have reached or exceeded your daily quota with just two meals. It really isn't difficult to reduce your caloric intake. You don't always have to decrease the amount you eat, just the types of food.

Q. Why am I telling you to watch calories as part of a stress-management program?

A. It's because you are what you eat. Your immune system, cardiovascular system, endocrine system, and nervous system — the major systems that have to work optimally under stress — depend upon the foods you eat. If you want them to work on demand, you have to take care of them. That means being aware of every aspect of your nutrition program.

Is It Working? Everywhere you turn, someone is anxious to provide you with definitive nutrition advice in exchange for your hard-earned dollars. This section will teach you how to evaluate what is best for you. From now on, whenever you are presented with a new and improved version of dietary advice, you will have a definitive test at your disposal. Before you begin, you'll need a heart rate monitor, a watch, and access to either a stationery bicycle or a treadmill with an odometer attached. The routine will always be the same. Warm up until your heart rate reaches 75 percent of the maximum. This is the moderate stress range. Then, note the time and maintain that heart rate as closely as you can for exactly five minutes. You are going to measure two variables: 1) the distance traveled during the five minute test, and 2) the time it takes for your heart rate to return to 50 percent of the maximum. Make every attempt to keep the conditions exactly the same each time you take this test. This is especially important with respect to the warm up and cool down phase of the regimen. You also should note your fluid consumption and medications. You could use virtually any exercise for this test. The reason stationary fitness equipment is recommended is because weather conditions are no longer a variable.

First, take this test after eating your favorite foods. Then, follow the food guidelines suggested in this section, if they are different. As a result of eating healthier foods and smaller portions, your entire body should function at a greater level of efficiency. At the same heart rate, you will be able to cover a greater distance, and your heart will recover faster. Use this test to evaluate your performance at different times of the day or after a variety of different foods. It's also a great way to check out the claims made by those selling supplements.

Remember, exercise is a form of physical stress. Consequently, you actually are testing the effects of specific foods upon your ability to perform and recover from stress. What works during exercise also will serve you well in the corporate boardroom, negotiating with your teenager, or dealing with the myriad of daily stressors that simply are unavoidable. No, the test is not perfect. Each time you do this brief work-out, there will be a modest training effect, which might confound your measures. So vary the sequence, and then repeat certain dietary regimens to control for circadian, monthly, or seasonal effects.

You'll be amazed when you discover what a profound impact food can have upon your body. In all likelihood, you will see a greater magnitude of effect with increasing amounts of stress. So, repeat the evaluation keeping your heart rate in the low as well as high stress ranges. Keep track of the results.

Red, Red Wine: The consumption of alcohol has been controversial since the first fermented berry juice was ingested. While a bit of a nip creates a physical effect that may allow you to be more openly emotional in social situations, too much leads to the short-term misery of a hangover, or the long-term embarrassment when you realize you really did dance naked on a table.

A lot of media attention has been given lately to the connection between alcohol and the reduction of coronary arterial disease. At first, the theory was that the alcohol itself flushed out the arteries, but research now shows that the effective element is something called flavonoids, which are found in red wine and dark beer. In general, the more intense the color of the beverage, the more flavonoids it contains. Red wine, for example, provides more flavonoids than white because the skins, seeds, and stems of the grapes are left in during the wine-making process. It's these elements of the grape which contain the highest concentrations of flavonoids. A similar accumulation of flavonoids occurs in the processing of dark beer - the longer the hops, barley, and malt are left in the liquid, the more flavonoids are present. This is neither a license nor a recommendation to increase consumption of alcoholic beverages. Consuming more than two ounces of alcohol a day has serious, detrimental effects on the brain and liver. The benefits of flavonoids in the diet can be obtained from a variety of other sources. Purple grape juice has about one-third of the anti-clotting capability of red wine. Broccoli, onions, apples, and garlic, plus the skins of fruit and green and black teas also contain large concentrations of flavonoids.

Winning The Daily Challenge Using Food

1. 7:00 A.M. *Everyone's heard that they should drink at least eight glasses of water daily. Actually, that's wrong. If you exercise on a regular basis, you need at least two or three times that on a daily basis. Mild dehydration is probably the single most common cause of feeling weak and tired. So before you even think about getting dressed, grab that big plastic cup you got at the gas station, fill it up with water, and chug it down.*

106

2. 8:15 A.M. *Eat a breakfast that contains complex carbohydrates and a small amount of protein. These more rapidly will be converted into blood glucose than will be protein and fat. Realize as you eat your breakfast that you are putting fuel into your body to enable you to make it through lunch. Your options would include a bagel, fruit, or a bowl of cereal. Oatmeal, grits, and even a stack of three pancakes will work as well, provided that you ease up on the butter and syrup. As much as 76 percent of the calories in pancakes are in the form of carbohydrates. If you wash it down with a glass of orange juice, you'll be in good shape.*

3. 10:00 A.M. *It's time for a break, and you're feeling a little hungry. Stay away from the vending machine, which dispenses junk food. Instead, walk down to the cafeteria, and get a container of non-fat yogurt. This will provide you with protein to help build muscle. You don't want too much protein, or else it will be converted into fat. A cup of yogurt is just about what you need.*

4. 11:00 A.M. *That protein you consumed an hour earlier needs water in order for it properly to be utilized by the body. If you eat protein without water, it could put a bit of a strain on your kidneys and liver. Not only that, but the fluid will help prevent dehydration, which is a primary cause of weakness and fatigue. This also would be a good time to eat a banana, which not only is a very good source of carbohydrate, but also of potassium, which helps keep your body fluids in a state of good balance.*

5. 11:30 A.M. *Time for a coffee break. Remember that caffeine is a stimulant, and high dosages potentially can be harmful. But some research findings do indicate that the amount of caffeine in two strong cups of coffee (which, by the way, would be about 200 mg. of caffeine) actually may help you burn more fat when you exercise. This is based upon data from Wichita State University. It does this by stimulating an increase in the levels of fatty acids circulating in the blood. There's also evidence from McMaster University in Ontario that a little caffeine may make you work a bit harder in the gym, enabling you to get more benefit from your workouts. By decreasing fatigue, you're able to last longer. But realize that excessive caffeine also can affect your cardiovascular system in adverse* *ways. But forget this regimen if you already are consuming six to eight cups of coffee each day just to survive. That extra caffeine that you're putting into your body isn't going to do any good at all.*

6. Noon. *Time for a workout. But remember that for every 20 minutes of exercise, you need between four to six ounces of water. And remember that if the water is cool, it will be absorbed much faster than if it's warm.*

7. 1:30 P.M. *Time for a 30 minute lunch. You need at least 100 calories in the form of carbohydrate, which is precisely what your body is screaming for right now. Especially after a workout, which is when you need to replenish the glycogen stores that you have been using up. So look for a pasta salad or baked potato or rice. If you order a sandwich, make sure it's made with whole wheat bread. Remember that my philosophy is predicated upon energy expenditure followed by recovery. You need that carbohydrate in order to get maximal recovery. And don't forget to mix a little protein in your lunch as well. This will help to build up new muscle as well as keep you alert. That means some low-fat cottage cheese or, perhaps, a slice of turkey or chicken in that sandwich.*

8. 4:00 P.M. *There's a natural biological rhythm in the body that causes your blood sugar to drop in the afternoon. If your work situation allows it, try to get a little exercise. Climb a flight of stairs or, even better, walk outside and expose yourself to a little sunlight. The sunlight will help with the production of vitamin D, which your body needs in order to strengthen bone. You'll also rev up your cortisol, which will provide you with a source of energy because this is the steroid that converts stored energy into usable glucose. Then have a small snack--low-fat yogurt, a slice of cheddar cheese, or, perhaps, some skim milk. This will provide you with some protein again to help build up your muscles.*

9. 6:30 P.M. *It's now time for a well-earned dinner. Start with a salad. Spinach is good, and, while you're at it, add a few sunflower seeds or walnuts and then pour a little olive oil vinaigrette on. You are adding a little fat to your diet, but you're also giving yourself a pretty good dose of vitamin E. This natural antioxidant not only helps to neutralize free radicals, but it helps the body to better utilize oxygen. There are lots of* *options for healthy eating, but you might want to consider some stir-fried beef with broccoli and green peppers. Beef is an excellent source of protein, and a three-ounce serving will give you more than 40 percent of the RDA of vitamin B12. This vitamin helps to burn off fat and gives rise to red blood cells, which will help with your endurance. The broccoli will provide 120 percent of the RDA for vitamin C, while a single green pepper will provide another 90 percent. That vitamin C not only will help neutralize free radicals, it will help reduce the inflammation that often occurs if you exercise excessively. Finally, add a potato. It's an excellent source of complex carbohydrate, and it also contains more vitamin C, as well as potassium and iron. If it happens to be a sweet potato, it will give you a pretty good dose of beta-carotene, which is another antioxidant.*

10. 9:00 P.M. *It's time for a snack or, if you prefer, you might just want to call it dessert. Frozen yogurt might work, or have a fruit bar. These are good sources of carbohydrate, which, ultimately, will help facilitate your falling asleep.*

COPING WITH STRESS IN RELATIONSHIPS

Stress can induce changes in behavior that can have an adverse effect upon your relationships. Relationships at work, with family, or just casual acquaintances can be threatened. By making just a few adjustments, the same information can be applied to the relationships you have with a business partner, a co-worker, or a child. Here is a listing of some of the stress-induced behaviors that can affect your relationships:

Isolation	Lower sex drive
Intolerance	Nagging
Resentment	Blaming
Loneliness	Distrust
Lashing out	Less contact with friends
Hiding	Lack of intimacy
Clamming up	Using people

To Thine Own Self Be True: Unfortunately, relationships sometimes can be a major source of stress. Some people are manipulative, deceptive, or overly controlling. Such relationships can take a serious toll on your health if you find yourself on the receiving end of these tactics.

If your answer to any of the following questions is 'yes,' you may need to take steps to modify your response.

1. **Have you ever purchased something you didn't really want?**

2. **Have you ever accepted a food or beverage item when you didn't want to?**

111

3. Have you ever agreed to do something that was counter to your value system?

4. Have you ever regretted not taking action?

Now reflect upon why you responded the way you did:

What emotions allowed you to be manipulated?

What kept you from holding your ground or speaking your mind?

If someone wanted you to do something against your will, how best would that person accomplish this goal?

Reflecting upon the answers to these questions will enable you to identify the problem. Now, set about to fix it. A very simple strategy is to employ acting skills. Recall that occasion when you did speak your mind, and you achieved your objective. Recall when, under similar circumstances, you were able to do what you believed was right. Create a screenplay, and practice. Before entering a situation, practice, practice, and practice. You will become what you believe you are. And by recreating the behaviors associated with success, you will drive the physiology of success. It will happen. But this is something that has to be learned. And learning requires practice.

The rules for dealing with such problems are quite involved and have to be tailored for each situation. Nonetheless, here are some general guidelines:

- Do what you believe is right, not what is expected.
- Your choices are always yes, no, or none of the above.
- You do not have to give a reason for your choice.
- You do not have to apologize for your choice.
- Sleep on it before deciding.

- Read between the lines, but be careful of making inappropriate assumptions.
- Watch for signs of deception.
- Recognize your vulnerability.

It's a Mad, Mad World: Before you start working on the problem, get your anger under control. Realize that anger is a normal and healthy emotion. It is when there's a mismatch between your anger (or its expression) and the circumstances that a problem will arise. For example, you have been wronged by a co-worker, and you misdirect your wrath at a family member.

There are some interesting differences between men and women with respect to the expression of emotions, especially anger. Both get angry with about the same frequency - usually six or seven times a week, and the reasons behind the anger and its intensity are about the same. The differences lie in the manner in which anger is expressed.

Men are more inclined to shout and pound their fists. Women are more likely to cry or keep their anger to themselves. Also, women are more likely to express their anger in private and to someone who is not the source of the anger. And the greater the intensity of anger within the woman, the longer it takes her to recover. This isn't so with men. However, regardless of how anger is expressed, the toll this emotion takes on the body is the same.

❑ Inappropriate expression of anger is emotionally harmful, while justifiably expressed anger can be beneficial.

❑ Whether appropriate or not, anger unleashes chemical changes that place stress on the coronary system.

113

- The number and type of situations that cause you to feel angry can indicate your risk for coronary disease.

- You can train yourself to respond to situations with emotional responses other than anger.

The following questionnaire has been devised by Redford Williams, the author of *Anger Kills*, as a means by which a person can measure his level of hostility.

Count the number of times you answer yes:

1. Have you ever been so angry at someone that you've thrown things or slammed a door?
2. Do you tend to remember irritating incidents?
3. Do little annoyances have a way of adding up during the day, leaving you frustrated?
4. In the express line in the grocery store, do you count to see if anyone has more than 10 items?
5. If a person who cuts your hair trims off too much, do you fume about it for days afterwards?
6. When a driver cuts you off, do you honk your horn?
7. Have you dropped any friends because they just didn't live up to your expectations?
8. Do you find yourself getting annoyed at little things your spouse does that get under your skin?
9. Do you feel your pulse climb during an argument?
10. Are you often irritated by incompetence?
11. If the cashier gives you the wrong change, do you assume he's probably trying to cheat you?
12. If someone doesn't show up on time, do you plan the angry words you're going to say later?

If you scored three or less, then you probably do not have a problem. But a score of four to eight is an indication that your level of anger may very well be in the range that can cause coronary arterial disease. A score of nine or more puts you at very high risk.

Reducing Anger: The next time you find yourself becoming very angry, ask yourself each of the following questions:

1. Is this really worth getting worked up over?

2. Is my anger justified?

3. Will an angry outburst make any positive difference?

Only if you answer 'yes' to all three of these questions should you go ahead and have an angry outburst. But if your answer to any one of those questions is 'no,' then chill out. Actually, you already will have started to do it. Pausing long enough to ask yourself those questions takes the emotional edge off. If you still find yourself fuming, then find a distraction. Read a book, go for a walk, or do some meditation exercises. Here's another option. Get it out of your system physically. Hit golf or tennis balls, chop wood. Hit a punching bag, or pound a pillow with your fists. Scream if that will help, but to avoid triggering a panic attack in those nearby, bury your face in a pillow, or do it in some isolated location. Do remember, however, that carrying this approach *too* far can result in an actual increase in your anger. Monitor yourself carefully.

Sometimes, people have difficulty expressing anger. In many instances, expression of anger in the past has resulted in dire consequences: punishment as a child, loss of a job, break up of a relationship, or criminal charges. The stakes can be considerably higher than expressing happiness. First, you must overcome barriers to expressing anger, and then identify healthy outlets and appropriate means of expression.

- Realize that you don't always have to be pleasant, although despite the conventional wisdom, there are ways of expressing anger without necessarily causing offense.

- Maintain a realistic perspective about possibly upsetting those you care about. Failure to communicate your feelings shows an attitude of indifference, which can be destructive to any relationship.

- When expressing anger, be assertive, but not aggressive. Stay focused on the issues, but avoid being accusatory.

- Stop projecting into the future and imagining worst case consequences. If your anger is justified, the issue important, and speaking out may well help to rectify the problems, then the cost benefit ratio definitely will be in your favor.

- Calm yourself so that you can move into a higher level of processing, and carefully weigh the options. You're at the top of the food chain because you have a large, well- developed brain. Use it.

- Sometimes it's ok to do nothing.

- Accept responsibility for your actions.

Prepare For Your Defense: Sometimes, life is not fair, and, despite playing by the rules, you fall victim to those deliberately trying to undermine you. Here's what you do when all else fails, and you encounter a vindictive person.

Make sure you document everything that happens when your efforts are being undermined by a co-worker or supervisor. You need to include the date and time and, as best as you can recollect, exactly what was said. It is also a good idea to make a notation of other individuals who might have witnessed the event.

By writing things down, you will have a record that you can more objectively analyze in your attempt to seek a solution to the problem. Furthermore, you will realize that you are not going crazy - there really is something seriously wrong in the workplace. If the worst-case scenario occurs, and you are forced out of your job, by having things documented, you may be able to convince someone in the administration to respond. If you do decide upon legal action, then that record will be worth its weight in gold should you need to back up some of your claims. Hopefully, by following the recommended advice, this ultimate step will not be necessary.

There are some people who will not respond to even the most constructive intervention. But it is still important to do something; and, by using some of the recommended approaches, at the very least, you are putting yourself in the driver's seat. You are not shrugging your shoulders, walking away from the situation, and adopting the attitude, "Well, there's nothing I can do. If I say anything, if I do anything, I'll lose my job." Instead, you are engaging in behaviors that put you in control. To do otherwise will reinforce a feeling of helplessness.

Avoid These Pitfalls

- **Bill of Rights:** You do not have the right to always have your way. Conflicts should be resolved so everyone has at least some of their needs met.

- **Generalizations:** Avoid labels. Personality is a function of the environment. Yes, a person may act like an idiot when serving on a committee with you, but such labels zero in on only a limited part of that person.

- **Dichotomous Thinking:** Everything is black or white. People are angels or devils. It may seem that way, but that's because of the way you filter the information available to you. People really are different shades of gray. Parts may be good; parts may be bad.

- **Embellishment:** The more bizarre your behavior, the more you may have to justify your actions. The result is a tendency to collect only that information which will support your point of view and, if you are unsuccessful, will exaggerate the other person's actions.

- **Assigning Blame**: It is quite likely that the other person did not intentionally make you angry. In fact, they didn't make you angry at all. You made yourself angry through your interpretation of their behavior. So stay with the issues. Criticize *their behavior*, if warranted, but avoid *criticizing them*.

BURNOUT IN MARRIAGE

Burnout in marriage should be the rule, not the exception. I can't imagine a more incompatible relationship than that which exists between a man and a woman. Boys and girls grow up with different emphases on what they should be doing with their lives; we look different; we act different; and perhaps most importantly, we think in quite different ways. Yet, for some bizarre reason, marriages do persist, despite the fact that the person you may be living with on your 40th anniversary is not the same person you courted. That's because we change, which, in turn, alters the dynamics of the entire relationship. You start off being married to a lover and friend. When the children arrive, you find yourself being married to a father or a mother. The children may become the focus of attention for the next 20 to 30 years.

Humans are one of the few species that even attempt to endure the constant change that occurs in marriage and enter into a life-long, monogamous relationship. Of course, not all marriages do endure, so let's look at some of the reasons why some do, and some don't. I don't wish to imply that marriage should or should not be a goal. Some people have personality traits that are not suited for this kind of relationship. Others are better off single, and there is nothing wrong with the 'single' lifestyle. Assuming you have decided that you do want to be married - and for the right reasons - or that you want your current marriage to be successful , beware of potential pitfalls and how best to minimize stress in the relationship.

Types Of Partnerships: There are three general types of partnerships.

1. One type is typlified by two members who work outside the home. Both the husband and the wife share in earning money; they share the household chores, the child-rearing tasks, and making friends, as well. In other words, their lives are very closely intertwined at just about every level.

2. The second type of relationship is one in which responsibilities are divided on the basis of particular tasks. The common denominator is the home and family unit, but one individual goes out and earns the money while the other takes care of the home. They may even have different friends.

3. The third type of relationship is made up of two very independent individuals where each partner lives his or her own life, keeping separate bank accounts, and having separate circles of friends. They share only what happens to be convenient, and, for some individuals, this might be just the home.

There is no right or wrong type of relationship. Each of these distinct types works very well for some couples. Problems occur when the relationship changes, and what started out as a relationship where everything was shared now becomes a relationship where one partner seeks a greater degree of independence. The same is true where couples started out being more independent, and then one begins to desire more sharing. If that occurs, then the best solution might be separation. But before reaching that stage, I would like to discuss the process whereby loving relationships are established and their progression to a state of co-habitation.

Almost Like Being In Love: Infatuation is usually the first step in a love relationship because it is important to have some spark to ignite such a relationship. Unfortunately, some people never move past this first step. They thrive on the excitement of the new person in their life, feeling whole, believing that they have met the perfect person, that they will never be lonely or disappointed again, or that they will experience never-ending bliss. When this feeling ends, they assume it simply was not the right person and look for someone else, neglecting the steps that might lead to a long-term relationship. For others, once the infatuation dims, they settle for a numb, stagnant existence with their partner, remaining disappointed and cheated, believing love is an illusion or that they simply will not experience lasting love in their lifetime.

While meeting a special person can and should be a joyous time, it is important to realize that a deeper sense of intimacy is required to sustain most relationships for the long term. As you move beyond infatuation toward true love, couples often find that a new type of connection unfolds. Complete trust and unconditional love for your partner allows this process to happen. The trust and security that come with love open the door to new spontaneity, creativity, and excitement.

Looking For Love In All The Right/Wrong Places: The choice of partner for a long-term relationship is one of the most important decisions that you will make in your lifetime. While meeting a potential partner is rarely a planned or deliberate event, it is important to have an idea of what you are looking for in a mate before you start looking. Then, when you do meet someone, you can make some informed choices. This is not to say that reason is the only consideration. What we term as chemistry, attraction, and a spiritual connection between two people are equally important. But you do need to temper emotion with reason. Unfortunately, it is often difficult to truly know another person until you are strongly attached to them. Given this fact, it is helpful to make informed decisions early in the relationship, making it more likely that you and your partner are prepared for a committed relationship.

Asking certain questions and making careful observations are very useful when assessing a partner's capacity for a long-term relationship. Remember that people do change over time, and there is no way to know for certain without spending a large amount of time with the person. People typically present their most favorable side in the early stages of a relationship, so making observations about a person's actions on a day to day basis, along with what you can glean about their past, may be the most effective way to size up a partner. Remember, too, if you are looking only for positive traits in a person, you will find them; and if you are looking only for negative traits, that is what you will find. You must strive toward a balanced and reasonable perspective. Take some time, and make a list of what characteristics your partner must have, those that you would like them to have, but which are not essential, and those that you absolutely cannot accept.

Troubled Waters: There are many barometers of a troubled relationship. In general, a relationship is in trouble when two people are no longer a support for each other, when communication stops, or when two people become stuck in repeated cycles of conflict over which they feel powerless to change. Often people find themselves caught in a vicious cycle, where trying harder and harder works less and less. The end result may be anger and hurt feelings, or apathy and numbness. When you reach the point where nothing you do seems to work anymore, it is time to begin learning some new tools, possibly with the help of a trained therapist.

It is important to keep in mind that any long-term, committed relationship will confront people with parts of themselves and their partner that will challenge coping skills. Just because difficulties arise in a relationship does not necessarily mean it is unhealthy. Rather, a couple's *willingness* and *ability* to deal with the important issues are far more important factors. The following are some signs that a relationship is in trouble:

❑ *You Prefer To Spend Time Away from Your Spouse.* When you find yourself persistently building walls in your relationship by isolating yourself from your partner with work, hobbies, or children, your relationship is in trouble. While it is healthy to spend some time away from your partner, when you begin to avoid sharing time to avoid conflict or to meet too many needs not met in your relationship, there is a problem.

❑ *You Are Caught in Endless Cycles of Silent or Active Conflict.* When you find that all disagreements end in angry outbursts, hurt feelings, miscommunication, or a feeling of hopelessness, you need to be concerned. Most relationships cannot tolerate this pattern for extended periods of time.

❑ *Effective Communication Has Ceased.* When you stop sharing, listening, and discussing your emotions, thoughts, or interests with your partner, closeness will suffer.

❑ *Emotional Alienation Has Set In.* When you feel completely disconnected from your partner, you are essentially living together alone. If you don't feel you know what is going on emotionally in each other's lives, intimacy will suffer.

❑ *There Is Lack of Trust.* Basic trust and a belief that your partner has your interests at heart are crucial in a relationship. When trust suffers, closeness suffers. Honesty and genuineness are essential to any meaningful relationship.

❑ *A Climate of 'Me Versus You' Is Present.* When it is no longer 'us' and becomes 'me versus you,' the commitment of a long-term relationship begins to fade. In order for a healthy relationship to last, each partner's separate interests must somehow be balanced with what is in the best interest of the relationship. Remember, you are both on the same team. Competitiveness can greatly divide relationships.

If these circumstances apply to your relationship, you may be suffering from marital burnout. If you are not sure, take this quick test:

1. Are you tired of your marriage?
2. Does the relationship you have with your spouse make you feel depressed?
3. If not depressed, do you often feel run down?
4. Do you feel trapped in your relationship?
5. Do you feel worthless in your marriage?
6. Do you feel resentment towards your spouse?
7. Do you believe the marriage creates for you a hopeless situation?
8. Do you believe that you are helpless in dealing with the problems associated with your marriage?
9. Have you reached the point where you think you just can't handle things anymore?

If you answered yes to three or more of these questions, you and your partner have your work cut out for you.

If your partner is unwilling to be involved in resolving the conflicts, you will need to make a choice whether or not you can accept the relationship as it is or whether you need to terminate it. Going outside the relationship to meet unfulfilled needs is a choice for some, but serious consequences can follow this decision, even if you believe you have done it for the right reasons.

First, focus on the positive. No individual and no relationship, even a long-lasting marriage, are perfect, no matter what you have convinced yourself of or how it might appear to the outside observer. The reason that some couples are happy and others are not is largely because the happy couples focus on the positive aspects of the relationship. For example, you might be very frustrated because your spouse is disorganized. But when you start to reflect upon your spouse's warmth and sensitivity, that perspective may enable you to diffuse your anger.

Another important ingredient in a happy relationship is the willingness to express appreciation. It is not enough to assume that your partner knows how you feel. It is important to show the appreciation, as well. Do it verbally and through actions. Too often, we tend to voice criticism and express anger. Positive reinforcement always is more effective.

Talking to each other cannot be overemphasized. There has to be communication, and without it, the emotional and physical intimacy that a relationship needs to be based upon is going to disappear. Talking has to be a priority. Don't wait until there is simply a convenient time. Make the time available. Set aside 20, 30, or 60 minutes, whatever it takes. By simply doing this, you are communicating to each other that this aspect of the relationship is at least as important, if not more important, than those things you are taking the time away from.

Talk to your spouse and not a confidante. Or at least don't exclude your spouse from discussions. A lot of people, when they find themselves in a troubled relationship, will turn to a friend, partly because the friend is more likely to side with them and to offer sympathy. But all that individual is going to be able to do is speculate about why your partner has engaged in a particular pattern of behavior. The only person who can provide the critical information to resolve the problem is the one who is directly involved. When you do talk, don't attack the other person. Avoid criticism. Your goal is to help the relationship. Identify what it is that each of you wants, and then focus on what it is that needs to be done in order to achieve that objective. Avoid reminding the other person of past behaviors that may date back years or decades. The focus must be on the relationship, not personalities. This is not about assigning blame or taking credit. The objective is to build a solid relationship. Focusing upon individual issues increases the probability that the discussion will evolve into a debate.

The adage "variety is the spice of life" is absolutely true. Too many people get into a rut. I don't mean variety in the number of partners you have. I'm talking about varying the way you do things within the relationship. It might be breaking the routine of what you usually do on weekends, or the place you go on vacation. It might be the types of food you eat, or even where and when you have sex. Everyone needs a certain amount of emotional excitement in their life to counterbalance boredom and tedium. And don't forget to have fun. Seek out ways to make your marriage fun, adventuresome, and exciting. While there are times when you need a certain amount of excitement, there are also times when you may need tranquility. The same applies to a relationship. The marriage needs to have a solid foundation with each partner secure in the knowledge that the other person is going to be there. At the same time,

126

each one needs to build on that foundation. They need to build together, and they need to build individually. Each person needs a certain amount of personal growth as well as spiritual growth. In order to achieve this growth, it may be necessary to take different courses. Successful marriages work because there is a balance. There is a solid foundation, and there is opportunity within the marriage for each person to spread their wings and to develop their own interests, leisure activities, and, perhaps, even friends. A marriage that is founded only on security may stifle growth and development. At the same time, too much growth and development, especially on an individual basis, may make it difficult to keep the marital bond strong. There needs to be a foundation of commitment as well as the energy to grow. After reviewing all of the difficulties and attempting to resolve them, you and your partner may conclude that the relationship is a lost cause. Divorce may be the best course of action.

He Got the Goldmine; I Got the Shaft: Divorce is a very difficult transition. Even when a divorce eventually makes life better for a person, there are a number of losses that must be dealt with. People lose much more than a partner. Divorce may lead to a reduction in your standard of living, the loss of a home, important routines, and time with children or friends. As a result, feelings of shock, confusion, sadness, fear, and anger typically arise. Often the adjustment period following divorce can be much different, depending on whether you were the person who made the decision to end the marriage or whether your partner decided. For many, divorce is the beginning of an emotional roller coaster. The key to getting through this time is to deal with emotions directly. You also need to maintain or even expand your social support system in order to fill the void left by divorce. Moreover, seek out people to help you talk about the emotions you are feeling, and avoid overly distracting yourself with work, another relationship, or unhealthy coping mechanisms. Recognize that the first year following a divorce is a period of reorganization. While many decisions can't wait, major job, family, and lifestyle decisions are best postponed during this period.

Although time alone may be very difficult at first, it is important to take time to reflect upon your life and your priorities. This is particularly important if you have never been on your own. Learning to be comfortable with your 'alone time' is an important goal. You will be surprised at what comes up when you simply slow down and focus on what you feel.

In order to assist with the process of grief, it can be helpful to arrange one or more rituals to symbolize and to make real the loss. Like a funeral ceremony for the dead, a ritual makes the experience real and provides a concrete way of saying good-bye. You could take a hike to a favorite view point and recite a poem or a note you've written about the relationship ending, or you could schedule a ceremony to dispose of some pictures or mementos from the relationship. Be creative, do what works for you, and allow this to be an emotionally significant, ceremonious event. If it doesn't seem real the first time you try it, you may want to repeat the ritual a few more times. The timing for your ritual may vary, but many people find it useful to schedule a ritual on the day the divorce is finalized. Rituals such as this can provide an opportunity to feel important emotions, to say good-bye, and to move on.

Divorce will often get people thinking about who they were before the marriage. Indeed, it may be a good time to think about what you used to do for fun, what subjects you were passionate about, or what used to be meaningful in your life. Reflect on what you did to survive other tough times in your life. Most importantly, trust that things will improve. Remember that every loss in life involves the letting go of something old and the birth of something new. Did you used to enjoy exercising, reading, painting, music, or hiking? During this time of transition, you will need to fill the void left by the divorce with an increased awareness of who you are and what makes you happy. Look inward and use your support system to navigate through a new phase in life.

At various times, we all experience what is usually described as 'the blues.' The treatment of these minor, sub-clinical depressions should focus initially upon determining to what degree environmental factors are responsible for the symptoms. The initial approach could be, then, to respond to the stimulus in a different way.

Often, the symptoms cause us to be distracted and unable to properly perceive what may appear to others as an obvious solution to our problem. That's why an attentive listener, such as a friend, can be very helpful in guiding us along the most appropriate course, as well as in improving our sense of self-worth.

A subject of dispute is whether women experience more emotion than men or whether they simply are more aware of their emotions because they've not been taught to repress them. Whatever the cause, it is true that women seek more treatment related to their feelings than men, and certain emotional states are more likely to present in women.

PMS: Premenstrual Syndrome or PMS is not a disease but a collection of symptoms which may have multiple causes. It's unlikely that any one intervention effectively will deal with all of the symptoms, but here are several interventions which may help alleviate some of them:

- **Breathe deeply.** This can help alleviate depression and anxiety, two of the major symptoms associated with PMS.

- **Reduce caffeine and alcohol use**, both of which can trigger everything from headaches to irritability, anxiety, and even depression.

- **Reduce your salt intake** to help alleviate fluid retention and the bloated feeling that often accompanies PMS.

- **Eat calcium-rich foods** to reduce both fluid retention and moodiness.

- **Undertake moderate exercise**, which helps relieve cramps and has a definite effect on mood improvement through endorphins being released into the blood.

- **Eliminate refined sugars,** which have been linked to the onset of PMS-induced irritability, fatigue, and even depression.

- **Try chocolate.** Some nutritionists suspect that chemicals in chocolate directly can alleviate some symptoms of PMS. Don't overdo it, though. Too much refined sugar will offset the potential benefits.

- **Eat a baked potato**, but hold the butter and sour cream. The carbohydrates will help boost serotonin, which can alleviate symptoms of depression.

There Is A Season, Turn, Turn, Turn: Just as there are seasons to the annual cycle of our world, there are seasons of the emotional cycle. When an event launches us into an emotional high - the summer of emotion, full of lushness and excitement - that high eventually passes. Our feelings about the event fade like the passing of summer into autumn. Eventually, we move into the emotional equivalent of winter, when our feelings lie fallow before entering the season of spring, when other emotions may grow and create a new dimension. From this seasonal cycle of emotions, we develop memories and a perspective that lead to wisdom as the years pass. Emotional states have long been thought to be brought on by the physical changes of the annual seasons themselves. This has been confirmed by the recognition of Seasonal Affective Disorder (SAD), thought to involve, at least in part, changes in the body's production of melatonin. Normally inhibited by sunlight, the levels of this neurotransmitter increase within the brain during darker, winter months. SAD, which is an apt acronym for the syndrome, is characterized by:

- ❑   a feeling of sadness.
- ❑   a decrease in libido.
- ❑   social withdrawal.
- ❑   decreased concentration.
- ❑   greater daytime drowsiness.
- ❑   overall fatigue.

Often, the syndrome is accompanied by appetite increase, weight gain, and hyper-insomnia. Some studies have found that the symptoms can be alleviated through exposure to full-spectrum lighting, which readjusts melatonin levels within the body. However, neither light therapy nor drug manipulation of melatonin levels is always effective, indicating an interplay of various neurotransmitters.

Seeking Counseling Or Psychotherapy. Psychotherapy or counseling may be helpful for individuals suffering from an array of emotional difficulties. Individuals suffering from depression, anxiety, relationship problems, eating disorders, panic attacks, phobias, or addictions may benefit from the many treatment approaches that psychologists, social workers, religious leaders, and counselors offer. In addition, therapy can be of great benefit in dealing with stressful events and major life transitions. These may include, for example, job or relationship loss, parenting issues, stress-related illness and physical symptoms, or death and grief. Therapy often can help people adjust more quickly and effectively to adverse events.

In general, when emotional issues begin to interfere with individual, family, work, or social functioning, therapy is indicated. In addition, treatment clearly is indicated for those who are experiencing recurrent thoughts of harming themselves or others, and/or become unable to care for their basic needs. Individuals who need therapy are often caught in a vicious cycle in which their efforts to bring about personal change on their own are increasingly ineffective. In spite of their many attempts to change, people often find that they lack the tools to make changes. In essence, they need the objective perspective of a trained professional. While there are many different treatment approaches, most therapies provide an opportunity to identify ineffective coping patterns and assistance in learning new, more effective methods of responding in a safe, accepting, and supportive environment. Ultimately, a more objective perspective of oneself is gained, and important decisions in life are made more consciously. In short, therapy can help you help yourself.

Seven Ways To Deal With Depression And Anxiety

1. **Translate your emotions into language.** Talk out loud or simply write the problem down. This will enable you to view the problem through a different sensory modality, for example, the auditory or visual system, giving you a different perspective from which to identify causes and/or solutions.

2. **Identify the emotion you are experiencing.** Are you feeling sad, angry, fearful, guilty, embarrassed, or a combination of these or others?

3. **Identify the source of the problematic emotion.** Are you angry at yourself for not accomplishing a goal? Are you fearful or sad about the consequences for not having done so? Are you feeling guilty because you failed? And remember that what really causes you to blow up at the end of the day may very well be some event you've been mulling over all day long.

4. **Identify the negative thoughts you might be experiencing and hold them up to reality.**

5. **Identify those thoughts, which are grossly exaggerated** and replace them with more rational thoughts. For example, if you happen to be late for a family gathering, don't assume that your family will think that you don't love them. Recognize that they will probably accept that your tardiness was due to reasons outside of your control.

6. **Re-think the entire scenario.** Just as a result of going through these steps at this point, you probably have already avoided a major emotional crisis.

7. **Once you figure out what went wrong, take corrective action.** Learn from your mistakes, and set about to make sure that it doesn't happen again. Remember that even your biggest blunder can always serve as a bad example for future choices.

EXCUSES TO DO NOTHING

You know what you need to do, but you just don't seem to get around to doing it. The following are some of the more common excuses along with counter-arguments:

It's boring. It certainly will be with that attitude. It doesn't have to be. Exercise, for example, can be done with a friend. Make it a learning experience, and keep detailed notes on how you progress. That's why I encourage you to use a heart rate monitor. Still boring? Even if it is, is that worse than the toll unmanaged stress is going to take?

People will think I'm weak if I can't handle stress without this program. If they do, chances are they are transferring their attributes to you. It's a common ploy called 'projection.' Don't fall for it. The world has changed so rapidly that your body hasn't had a chance to adapt. Human minds have created the Information Age, along with all the pitfalls. Use yours to make sure your journey is as smooth as possible. It's your choice.

I don't need this program. Then why are you reading this? If you think you *might* need it, you probably *do*.

I don't have enough time. That's the worst excuse of all. Fatigue is a common symptom of stress. Anything you can do to counter it will enable you to use your time more efficiently. By employing the exercise and nutritional guidelines recommended in this program, you will fall asleep faster and obtain more restful sleep. After a few weeks, you will need less sleep. Yes, the program described in this book will help you create time.

SURVIVING THE MEDICAL SYSTEM

The medical paradigm embraced by the established medical authorities in the United States is simultaneously a spectacular success and a dismal failure. It has produced the best medical care to be found anywhere in the world, yet infant mortality rates in this nation are comparable to those of Third World countries.

The successes are to be found in trauma centers where physicians have acquired the skills to repair everything from broken bones to damaged hearts. And we are increasingly successful in diagnosing disease and predicting, through gene technology, the probability that certain illnesses might occur. But little success has been achieved in devising treatments for chronic illnesses, especially those that involve multiple organ systems and which appear to be associated with emotional distress.

Ironically, the successes of Western medicine stem from the same approaches that account for its failures. By focusing on the separation of mind and body, the result has led to the body being dissected into well-defined, component parts. The endocrine system, the immune system, the nervous system, and the cardiovascular system are not only designations which carve our bodies into parts; they also define the boundaries of common medical specialties, as well. This reductionistic approach has enabled medicine to unravel the molecular mysteries of a variety of diseases and to devise intervention strategies based upon these discoveries. But in focusing solely upon isolated systems and their corresponding parts, we have lost sight of the fact that each of us is considerably more than the sum of our biological parts.

Consequently, many practitioners of modern medicine who take great pride in adhering to the rigors of this approach cannot incorporate the notion that a disease may be triggered by a twisted soul or by spiritual bankruptcy. These are terms that simply cannot be defined and for which no chemical or biological markers exist. Today, disease is attributed to the invasion of the body by pathogens, which, during previous eras, might have been labeled as *'evil spirits'* or a *'curse.'* The focus is upon the external causes of disease, both during the diagnosis and the treatment of the illness. While pathogens are certainly important triggers, the powerful healing system that lies within each of us is largely ignored.

The discovery of pathways that bind the brain and the immune system rescues the behavioral approach to disease from the shadowy practices of witch doctors and places it squarely within the rational tradition of Western medicine. We are witnessing the birth of a new integrative science - psychoneuroimmunology - which *begins* with the premise that neither the brain nor the immune system can be excluded from any scheme accounting for the onset and course of disease. The first, and, in the long run, the most valuable, clinical spin-offs of Psychoneuroimmunology will be in disease prevention - initially, in the development of ways to manage stress.

I do not advocate that behavioral interventions simply replace traditional treatments, especially those of proven efficacy. What I am advocating is that you engage in activities which enable you to maintain an optimal state of health. Healing should be like an investment portfolio - diversified. Rely upon your physicians, but invest in your own health by strengthening your mental and physical assets through exercise, nutrition, and the resources that best inspire your emotional forces with hope and guidance.

Ideally, you and your doctor will function in a balanced partnership striving to achieve the same goal - your health and well-being. To this relationship, the doctor brings years of learning and experience in working with the human body. But this is no more valuable than the knowledge of your own body that you have acquired. Your doctor can serve you based only upon what he or she can learn from you - and your healing directly is enhanced by your involvement in the treatment.

Pay attention to the questions the doctor asks you. The answers you give will provide vital information and valuable clues to your health. And make sure you get all of the information · you need. During physical exams and consultations, anxiety can cause you to forget questions you want to ask or the answers to those you do. Take along a list of what you want to discuss, and take notes on the answers. Better yet, let a tape recorder act as your back-up memory.

Don't depend on your doctor as your sole source of information. Accept responsibility, and do some detective work so you can ask intelligent questions and better understand treatment alternatives.

Reward your doctor with gratitude. Unfortunately, doctors too rarely hear from patients when things are going well. Let your doctor know what is improving for you, as well as what still needs attention. Thank him for helping you get better. Acknowledge her insight. Small tokens of appreciation can pay huge dividends in the emotional bond which may develop and the extra attention you're likely to receive.

PERTINANT REFERENCES

Ader, R., (Ed.) (2007). Psychoneuroimmunology IV. New York: Academic Press.

Alexopoulos, G.S. 2001. New concepts for prevention and treatment of late-life depression. *American Journal of Psychiatry* 158(June):835.

Andrews G, Sanderson K, Slade T, Issakidis C 2000. Why does the burden of disease persist? Relating the burden of anxiety and depression to effectiveness of treatment. Bull World Health Organ;78(4):446-54.

Antonijevic, I. 2006. Depressive disorders – is it time to endorse different pathophysiologies? Psychoneuroendocrinology 31: 76.

Archer, J.C. 2005. An integrated review of indirect, relational, and social aggression. Personality and Social Psychology Review 9: 212.

Aron, A. et al. 2005. Reward, motivation, and emotion systems associated with early-stage intense romantic love. J. Neurophysiol 94:327.

Black, A., *et al.* 2000. Calorie restriction reduces the incidence of proliferative disease: Preliminary data from the NIA CR in nonhuman primate study. Gerontological Society of America annual meeting. Nov. 17. Washington, D.C.

Black, P.H., and Garbutt, L.D. 2002. Stress, inflammation and cardiovascular disease. J. Psychosom. Res. 52: 1-23.

Boren, E. and Gershwin, M.E. 2004. Inflamm-aging: Autoimmunity, and the immune-risk phenotype. Autoimmunity Reviews, 3:401-406.

Brown, A.S., *et al.* 2000. Maternal exposure to respiratory infections and adult schizophrenia spectrum disorders: A prospective birth cohort study. *Schizophrenia Bulletin* 26(No. 2):287-295.

Brown, S.L., *et al.* 2003. Providing social support may be more beneficial than receiving it: Results from a prospective study of mortality. *Psychological Science* 14(July):320-327.

Butler, T. et al. 2005. Fear related activity in subgenual anterior cingulated differs between men and women. Neuroreport 16:1233-36.
.
Cohen, S., *et al.* 2006. Positive emotional style predicts resistance to illness after experimental exposure to rhinovirus or influenza A virus. *Psychosomatic Medicine* 68(November/December): 809-815.

Cavigelli, S.A., and M.K. McClintock. 2003. Fear of novelty in infant rats predicts adult corticosterone dynamics and an early death. *Proceedings of the National Academy of Sciences* 100(Dec. 23):16131-16136.

Coe, C. 2004. Biological and social predictors of immune senescence in the aged primate. Mechanisms of Ageing and Development. 135:95-98.

Collins, S.M. 2001. Stress and the gastrointestinal tract. Modulation of intestinal inflammation by stress: basic mechanisms and clinical relevance. Am. J. Physiol Gastrointest Liver Physiol 280, G315-318.

Cordle, C.T., *et al.* 2002. Immune status of infants fed soy-based formulas with or without added nuclotides for 1 year: Part 2: Immune cell populations. *Journal of Pediatric Gastroenterology and Nutrition* 34(February):145-153.

Damasio, A.R., *et al.* 2000. Subcortical and cortical brain activity during the feeling of self-generated emotions. *Nature Neuroscience* 3(October):1049-1056.

Danner, D.D., D.A. Snowdon, and W.V. Friesen. 2001. Positive emotions in early life and longevity: Findings from the nun study. *Journal of Personality and Social Psychology* 80(May):804..

Dantzer, R. et. al. 2007. Cytokines, sickness behavior, and depression. In: Psychoneuroimmunology,, 4th editions, Academic Press, NY. 281.

Davidson, R.J., *et al.* 2003. Alterations in brain and immune function produced by mindfulness meditation. *Psychosomatic Medicine* 65(July/August):564-570.

de Kloet, E.R. et al. 2005. Stress, genes and the mechanism of programming the brain for later life. Neurosci Biobehav Rev. 29: 271-81.

De Rubeis, R.J. et al. 2005. Cognitive therapy vs. medications in the treatment of moderate to severe depression. Arch Gen Psychiatry 62: 409-16.

Debiec, J. 2005. Peptides of love and fear: vasopressin and oxytocin modulate the integration of information in the amygdala. Bioessays 27:869-73.

Doyle, W.J., D.A. Gentile, and S. Cohen. 2006. Emotional style, nasal cytokines, and illness expression after experimental rhinovirus exposure. *Brain, Behavior, and Immunity* 20(March):175-181.

Elavsky, S. et al. 2005. Physical activity enhances long-term quality of life in older adults:efficacy, esteem, and affective influences. Ann Behav Med 30: 138-45.

Franklin, T. 2006 Sex and ovarian steroids modulate brain derived neurotrophic factor (BDNF) protein levels in rat hippocampus und stressful and non-stressful conditions. Psychoneuroendocrinology 31: 38-53.

Freidman, H. 2008. The multiple linkages of personality and disease. Brain, Behavior, and Immunity, 22: 647.

Gilbertson, M.W., *et al.* 2002. Smaller hippocampal volume predicts pathologic vulnerability to psychological trauma. *Nature Neuroscience* 5(November):1242-1247.

Grant, I., *et al.* 2002. Health consequences of Alzheimer's caregiving transitions: Effects of placement and bereavement. *Psychosomatic Medicine* 64(May/June):477-486.

Gretan, F.R. .and M. Karin. 2004. IKK links inflammation and tumorigenesis in a mouse model of colitis-associated cancer. *Cell* 118(Aug. 6):285-296.

Halbreich, U. 2006. Major depression is not a diagnosis, it is a departure point to differential diagnosis – clinical and hormonal considerations. Psychoneuroendocrinology 31: 16-22.

Hall, N. R. 2008. Understanding Stress and Immunity. NursingSpectrum Press.

Hawkley, L.C. and Cacioppo, J.T. 2003. Stress and the aging immune system. Brain, Behavior and Immunity, 18: 114-119.

Kiechl, S., et al.2002. Toll-like receptor 4 polymorphisms and atherogenesis. *New England Journal of Medicine* 347(July 18):185-192..

Kiecolt-Glaser, J.K et al. 2003. Chronic stress and age-related increases in the proinflammatory cytokine IL-6. *Proceedings of the National Academy of Sciences* 100(July 22):9090-9095.

Kiecolt-Glaser, J.K. et al. 2005. Hostile marital interactions, proinflammatory cytokine production, and wound healing. Arch Gen Psychiatry 62: 1377-84.

Kubzansky, L.D., et al. 2007. Prospective study of post-traumatic stress disorder symptoms and coronary heart disease in the normative aging study. *Archives of General Psychiatry* 64(January):109-116.

Madden, K.S. 2003. Catecholamines, sympathetic innervation, and immunity. *Brain, Behav. Immun.* 17:5.

Marsland, A. et al. 2008. Antagonistic characteristics are positively associated with inflammatory markers independently of trait negative emotionality. Brain, Behavior, and Immunity. 22:753.

Meaney, M.J. 2001. Maternal care, gene expression, and the transmission of individual differences in stress reactivity across generations. Annu Rev Neurosci 24: 1161-92.

Meerlo, P., et al. 2002. Sleep restriction alters the hypothalmic-pituitary-adrenal response to stress. *Journal of Neuroendocrinology* 14(May):397-402.

Merrill, J.E. 2001. Production and influence of inflammatory cytokines in diseases of the adult central nervous system. In Psychoneuroimmunology, 3rd Edition. (R. Ader, D. Felten, N. Cohen, eds). Academic Press, New York.

Moldoveanu AI, Shephard RJ, Shek PN 2001. The cytokine response to physical activity and training. Sports Med . Feb;31:115

Onard, J., M. Schoneveld, and A. Kavelaars. 2007. Glucocorticoids and immunity. In: Psychoneuroimmunology, 4th edition, Academic Press, NY. 281

Ostir GV, Markides KS, Black SA, Goodwin JS. 2000. Emotional well-being predicts subsequent functional independence and survival. J Am Geriatr Soc;48(5):473-8.

Ownby, D.R., and C.C. Johnson. 2002. Exposure to dogs and cats in the first year of life and risk of allergic sensitization at 6 to 7 years of age. *Journal of the American Medical Association* 288(Aug. 28):963-972.

Peters, E.M. et al. 1993. Vitamin C supplementation reduces the incidence of post race symptoms of upper respiratory tract infection in ultra marathon runners. American Journal of Clinical Nutrition 57, 170.

Phelps, E.A. 2004. Human emotion and memory: interactions of the amygdala and hippocampal complex. Curr Opin Neurobiol 14: 198-202.

Phillips, D.P., *et al.* 2001. The Hound of the Baskervilles effect: A natural experiment on the influence of psychological stress on the timing of death. *British Medical Journal* 323(Dec. 22):1443.

Postolache, T, Komarow, H. and Tonelli, L. 2008. Allergy: A risk factor for suicide? Current Treatment Options in Neurology. 10:363.

Quirk, G.J., *et al.* 2003. Stimulation of medial prefrontal cortex decreases the responsiveness of central amygdala output neurons. *Journal of Neuroscience* 23(Sept. 24):8800-8807.

Sapolsky, R. M. 2004. Why Zebras Don't Get Ulcers: A Guide to Stress, Stress-Related Diseases, and Coping. W.H. Freeman and Co., New York.

Seligman, M. 1998. Learned optimism. Simon and Schuster, New York.

Shi, Y., J.E. Evans, and K.L. Rock. 2003. Molecular identification of a danger signal that alerts the immune system to dying cells. *Nature* 425(Oct. 2):516-521

Singer, T. et al. 2006. Empathic neural responses are modulated by the perceived fairness of others. Nature 439: 466-69.

Stoltz, P.G. 1997. The Adversity Quotient: Turning Obstacles Into Opportunity. John Wiley & Sons, New York.

Temoshok, L et. Al. 2008. Type C coping, alexithymia, and heart rate reactivity are associated independently and differentially with specific immune mechanisms linked to HIV progression. Brain, Behavior and Immunity. 22: 781.

Tucker, P.M., *et al.* 2007. Physiologic reactivity despite emotional resilience several years after direct exposure to terrorism. *American Journal of Psychiatry* 164(February):230-235.

Wallenstein, G. 2003. Mind, Stress and Emotions. Commonwealth Press, Washington DC.

Wan, R., S. Camandola, and M.P. Mattson. 2003. Intermittent food deprivation improves cardiovascular and neuroendocrine responses to stress in rats. *Journal of Nutrition* 133(June):1921-1929.

Watkins, L. et al. 2007. Neuroimmune interactions and pain: The role of immune and glial cells. In: In: Psychoneuroimmunology,, 4th editions, Academic Press, NY. 281.

Weisler, R.H., J.G. Barbee, and M.H. Townsend. 2006. Mental health and recovery in the Gulf Coast after hurricanes Katrina and Rita. *Journal of the American Medical Association* 296(Aug. 2):585-588.

Wetherell, M. and K. Vedhara. 2007. Stress-associated immune dysregulation can affect antibody and T-cell responses to vaccines. In: Psychoneuroimmunology,, 4th editions, Academic Press, NY. 281.

Weuve, J., *et al.* 2004. Physical activity, including walking, and cognitive function in older Women. *Journal of the American Medical Association* 292(Sept. 22/29)1454-1461.

Williams, L.M., *et al.* 2006. The mellow years? Neural basis of improving emotional stability over age. *Journal of Neuroscience* 26(June 14):6422-6430.

Zak, P.J. et al. 2005. Oxytocin is associated with human trust-worthiness. Horm Behav 48: 522-27.

Zald, D.H. 2003. The human amygdala and the emotional evaluation of sensory stimuli. Brain Res Rev 41: 88-123.

Ziv, Y. and Schwartz. 2008. Immune-based regulation of adult neurogenesis: Implications for learning and memory. Brain, Behavior, and Immunity. 22: 167.